MW01093796

Your Admissions Coach To PHARMACY SCHOOL

Everything You Need to Know
About Getting In

RYAN NGOV, PharmD | KATHY CHOW, PharmD

Reshape The Mind, Inc.
112 E. Live Oak Ave.
Arcadia, CA 91006
www.reshapethemind.com

Copyright © 2018 by Ryan Ngov and Kathy Chow

All rights reserved. No part of this book may be reproduced, stored in retrieval system, or transmitted in any form or by any means electronic, mechanical, photocopying, recording, or otherwise without prior written permission of the publisher and the authors. For information, contact support@reshapethemind.com or visit www.pharmacyinterview.com

The information contained in this book is for general education purposes only. While the information contained in this book is intended to be accurate at the time of publishing, nothing should be construed as legal, tax, or financial advice.

Printed in the United States of America

Library of Congress Control Number: 2018967073

ISBN 978-1-970084-00-9 (Paperback)
ISBN 978-1-970084-01-6 (Mobi)
ISBN 978-1-970084-02-3 (Epub)

First Edition December 2018

10 9 8 7 6 5 4 3

CONTENTS

WHY YOU NEED THIS BOOK

DURING OUR FIRST YEAR of pharmacy school, we would often commiserate about the difficulty of getting into pharmacy school and the lack of quality medical school admission guides for prospective pharmacy school students. Obviously, they were not written for pre-pharmacy students.

Then and there, we started to write what is now a comprehensive guide on how to get into pharmacy school. Fast forwarding almost a decade, not much has changed in regards to resources for prospective pharmacy school students. There is still a lack of clarity around several aspects of the pharmacy field, including financial details, the pros and cons of different pharmacy fields, and helping each prospective student decide if pharmacy school is the right fit for them. This book endeavors to help fill those gaps.

Pursuing a pharmacy degree is a huge investment of time, energy, and resources of all kinds. After many late nights of writing and researching, we've combined our pharmacy experience and knowledge with useful information, such as admission criteria and program affordability, collected from a wide variety of pharmacy schools and programs. By putting all of this information into a single source, our goal is to streamline the admissions process for you and guide you through the important decisions that you will make along the way.

As pharmacy students, we always wished that we had a guide. Now this book will serve as yours.

CONTACT US

www.reshapethemind.com

www.pharmacyinterview.com

https://www.facebook.com/PharmacySchoolCoach/

1

DON'T JUST SHINE, OUTSHINE.

"Shine bright like a diamond." – Rihanna

THE FACT THAT YOU are picking up this book tells us that you are serious about getting into pharmacy school, or, at least, seriously considering it. We must warn you that picking up this book may cause sleepless nights, elevated blood pressure, paranoia, self-doubt and an irrational fear of orange bottles with white labels. You will, however, learn a great deal about how to outshine others while applying to schools, which school is right for you, and all aspects of a career in pharmacy. We were in your shoes once, and pharm school information was scattered and scarce because there was such a limited selection of resources available to help us understand the application process, let alone a guide to standing out among thousands of applicants applying to pharmacy schools every year. That's why we wrote this book. This book will help you achieve your dream of becoming a pharmacist. This book is for YOU.

The application process can be very stressful for one big reason: Applicants don't know what to expect and what is expected of them. Clarity is power and that is exactly what you will gain after reading this book.

Let's get started.

Getting Started

We hate wasting time. More specifically, we hate wasting YOUR time (and money). So we're asking you—no, begging you—to read this book with deliberation and a sense of purpose. Every chapter has been carefully crafted to give you maximum information with minimal effort on your part. We can give you advice, but you must choose to absorb and **action it.**

Know what you don't know. Sit down with a pen and a piece of paper. Write out a game plan. Draw a roadmap of what you want to achieve and the knowledge you need to get there. This book was written in a manner that lets you dictate what you want to learn in what order. You can read it front to back, but you can also jump around. We recommend starting with the next section, *Mediocre to Total Badass in Five Simple Steps,* to get yourself ahead of the game. Check out *Is Pharmacy School Right for Me?* to determine whether your personality and a career in pharmacy mesh. *What Can I Do with a PharmD?* is where you can delve into other aspects of pharmacy besides the "pill counter" aspect. If you are wondering how much money pharmacists make (who wouldn't be?), go ahead and flip to the appropriately titled section, *How Much Does a Pharmacist Make?*

There is no particular order in which you should digest this book. Start off with any chapter that piques your interest. Use the tools we're handing you to determine whether pharmacy is for you. Then, read up on the application process and on the factors that affect your chance of acceptance into pharmacy school. We've consolidated numbers from all over the internet from GPA and PCAT stats to work experience and personal statements, etc. to make your life easier (we are now Google search masters).

In particular, the *Admitted GPA Table* will come in handy when you are deciding which school to apply to based on your GPA and geographic preferences. Schools are sorted by state, minimum GPA needed to apply, and average GPA of admitted students. We're handing you a veritable five-course meal compacted into a soup spoon, you just need to swallow.

The skills you obtain in this book will help you get your foot in the door whether for internships, pharmacy school interviews or job interviews.

Common Questions and Where to Find the Answers

Mediocre to Total Badass in Five Steps

You may have heard that the key to getting ahead is to get started.[1] The truth is a little more complex than that. Not only do you need to get started, you must also stay persistent and committed to your goals. While this may come across as kumbaya mumbo-jumbo, it's as important as getting straight A's in school. What's the use of having good grades if you don't harness that talent wisely? In order to get ahead, you must first **believe** that you can and will be accepted into pharmacy school. As Henry Ford once said, "Whether you think you can, or you think you can't ... you're right." [2]

Assuming Ford's quote is true, why do so many individuals limit their potential? Why do they talk themselves out of starting on lifelong dreams? The answer lies within human psychology. Success is 80% psychology and 20% mechanics.[3] If you are not motivated, you won't even bother to take the first step. On the other hand, if you believe that this is your calling, you **will** find a way.

Applying to pharmacy school is simple, but it is not easy. In this section, you will build a strong mindset through these mental hacks used by high achievers to stay ahead of their game:

1. Cultivate a Growth Mindset [4]

People with a growth mindset view struggles as opportunities for improvement; they view challenges as a natural part of becoming better. They increase their efforts and seek new strategies as they encounter obstacles. They are more likely to look for new challenges and are more likely to step out of their comfort zone. They are not afraid to ask questions (even if those questions seem stupid) and volunteer answers even when they are unsure. Research shows that a growth mindset is not only directly related to heightened academic performance but also achievements in other areas.

If you're interested in some light reading, Dr. Carol Dweck's book, *Mindset: The New Psychology of Success,* explores this concept. Dr. Dweck explores how adopting and cultivating a growth mindset results in higher levels of success in many aspects of life.

2. Establish Highly Effective Habits

Forty-five percent of what we do on a daily basis is autopilot and is driven purely by our habits.

Examples of obvious habits:

- Brushing your teeth before/after you get dressed
- Going for a run after work
- Taking multivitamins with your breakfast

Examples of less obvious habits:

- Procrastination (late assignments)
- Lack of prioritization (the important stuff is ignored)
- Messes that stress you out when you see them

Any of these habits sound familiar? Start with this shortcut—establish a few key, highly effective habits. These habits guarantee a huge payoff in both the short and long term. The five highly effective habits listed below will help you stay ahead of your competition:

a. Be Proactive [5]

Being proactive means you take full responsibility for your actions, you are in control of the scripts by which you live your life, be it the things you do, what you say, your response to what's happening, etc. Reactive people ask, "Why does this always happen to me?" whereas proactive people ask, "What's the lesson learned from this bad experience and how can I use that to my advantage?" Life doesn't happen TO proactive people, it happens FOR them.

b. **Be Certain and You Will Be Confident**

Do you ever fall prey to believing that you are not smart enough, educated enough or rich enough to go after something? Confidence is a sense of certainty that we can do something. This sense of belief doesn't come from what we have and what we own but rather what we create or generate. If your confidence account is low, you will always find a way to lose, to fail. More often than not, we quit before we even begin.

You must believe that you *are* enough and that you have what it takes to succeed. You must believe in your ability to figure things out. Use your past successes to generate confidence in your future endeavors. Practice generating this sense of certainty within yourself that you can accomplish anything you put your mind to. This is not to say that you will always get things done perfectly the first time but rather you will keep going until you arrive at a solution that you truly desire.

c. **Feel Gratitude**

Live every day with gratitude and your whole life will change. When you feel grateful for what you have, you'll become more optimistic and more motivated to achieve bigger and better things. Who are you grateful to have in your life? What amenities are you grateful to own/have? Now, isn't that a beautiful state of mind to be in? Imagine how beneficial it would be if you got into the habit of imbuing your life with such strong positivity every day. Wake up on the "right" side of the bed every day with this little trick and you'll be as content as a cat with a cup of cream.

For cats that are lactose intolerant, we're sorry.

d. **Work Smart, Not Hard**

Don't misunderstand this; it's good to work hard. But there is a stark difference between working hard mindlessly and working hard productively. Just because you are constantly running about doesn't mean you're making rapid progress. Take grocery shopping, for instance. Imagine driving to the grocery store each time you realized you needed an item—how much time and gas would you waste? The smarter shopper would create a grocery list and would add to it throughout the week to ensure everything was covered on their next trip to the grocery store.

What's on your To-Do List? Start a Stop-Doing List as well. List activities that junk up your life such as checking your personal social media every waking hour, getting sucked into Facebook/Instagram black holes, and going to sleep after 1:00 a.m.

e. **Build and Maintain High Energy Reserves**

We start each day with a set energy "budget" unlike some gifted individuals (looking at you, Energizer Bunny). Proper nutrition and exercise are essential to maintaining high energy levels in our bodies, which in turn power us through all the work we need to complete to accomplish our goals. Also, sleep is underrated. Good sleep not only improves your energy level, it also brings other benefits such as increased mental concentration, immune function, glucose metabolism, athletic performance, social interaction, and reduced risk of stroke, heart attack, and other inflammation issues.

Carpe Diem the heck out of each and every day. Solid physical and mental health will pay you back a thousand fold.

3. Set High Standards

If you want to stay ahead of the game and get into your targeted pharmacy schools, you must learn to demand more from yourself than you normally do. This means going beyond meeting minimum requirements, exceeding the targeted schools' expectations, and establishing new standards that will result in you being the BEST sustainable version of yourself. This will set you apart from all other applicants. To build the best version of yourself, try asking yourself the following questions on a daily basis to keep track of your own performance:

- Did I do everything I set out to do today to the best of my ability?
- Did I make any improvement on my yesterday self? How do I know?
- What is the one thing I feel the proudest of today?
- What is not great yet? What am I willing to do or stop doing to make it great?
- Am I on track with my goals and what is the ONE thing that must get done tomorrow no matter what?

If you don't track your behavior/performance in relation to your new standards, then it was pointless to set standards at all. Whatever gets measured gets managed.

4. Have a Strong "Why"

If you are not motivated to pursue your goal, you probably do not have a strong enough "why". Nothing worthwhile comes easy. It's a given that you will encounter obstacles while you work to achieve something great be it getting into a pharmacy school, securing a high-paying job, sculpting a beach bod or running a successful company. Many people quit halfway whenever they face major challenges, not because they aren't smart enough but because they lack conviction, because they don't truly believe in why they are trying to accomplish that goal. If you are not absolutely convinced that pharmacy is right for you, we recommend that you figure out if it is. Check out the two sections *Is Pharmacy School Right for Me?* and *What Can I Do with a PharmD?* which can help steer you in the right direction. Remember this: nothing has any meaning except the meaning you give it.

5. Stay FOCUSED

Pay attention to where your focus goes because that is where your energy flows. We achieve what we focus on. If you focus on academic excellence, you will most likely do very well in school. If you spend a lot of time playing video games, you will do well in that. A minute spent focusing on negativity or past regrets is a minute wasted. If you catch yourself dwelling on problems you can't do anything about, you should redirect your attention to something else that really matters, something that will get you closer to your goals.

2

IS PHARMACY SCHOOL RIGHT FOR ME?

"Sometimes you make the right decision, sometimes you make the decision right." – Phil McGraw

SIMPLY STATED, PHARMACISTS ARE medication experts and they perform the last check before medication reaches the patient. They commonly work in retail pharmacies, such as CVS, Walgreens, and Rite-Aid, or in hospitals. There are other opportunities available to pharmacists such as opening your own pharmacy and becoming a business owner. Other fields for pharmacists include veterinary pharmacy, pediatric pharmacy, managed care pharmacy, nuclear pharmacy, etc., but most of these fields are less common and you would need to do residency (an extra year or two after pharmacy school) to get into them.

Pharmacy schools teach the same menu of topics since they all have the ultimate goal of preparing you to pass your boards, a standardized test which will officially license you as a pharmacist. When you pass your boards, you transition from a medication amateur to an expert.

Let's chat about what personality traits most successful pharmacists have. Self-reflect and take some time to ponder on whether this career is right for you.

Personality Traits of Successful Pharmacists

Meticulous and Attentive to Detail

This is the core of healthcare careers in a nutshell. The patient is sick; they see the doctor; the doctor evaluates the patient and orders the appropriate medication(s). The pharmacist then prepares the medication for the patient while checking for a long list of things (drug-drug interaction, drug-food interaction, allergies, drug-disease interaction among other things) and fills the correct medication for the right patient and dispenses the medication to the patient with appropriate counseling.

Paying attention to details is a must to prevent mistakes. These mistakes can be anything from inappropriate dosing to prescribing a drug that is contraindicated for the patient to drug-drug interaction—even giving the wrong drug to the wrong patient! In the hospital, a Kathy Chow may be placed in the same room as a Cathy Chao, and they are both receiving dialysis and have a long list of medications. This is where pharmacists like us can request a room change for a patient to help prevent mistakes. Having these two patients in the same room is like waiting for a med-error nuclear bomb to explode.

Pharmacists play an important role as part of the healthcare team because nurses, doctors, and everyone else will look up to *you* to be the medication expert. For example, the nurses will call you asking whether Drug A can be refrigerated or how long Drug B can be stable in an IV bag. Doctors will ask you which medication to give if a patient is resistant to drug X, Y, Z or ask you how to dose a certain medication for a patient who has chronic kidney disease, is on dialysis, morbidly obese or anorexic. As a pharmacist, you need to be detail-oriented as there will be patients with very similar names, similar disease states, and similar-sounding drugs with similar properties. You are the gatekeeper who's supposed to sort all these things out, so it is imperative for you to be vigilant, present, and fastidious.

People Person/Team Player

Do you enjoy talking to and helping people? Do you prefer to work in a team/group? As a pharmacist, you'll be doing that every day. You'll be interacting with pharmacy technicians, nurses, doctors, and, most often, patients. Everyone is working toward improving the patient's health together. Thriving in an environment that promotes teamwork and having people skills is a must.

Love of Teaching

A big part of being a pharmacist is educating others about their medications. Because most people haven't gone through 6–8 years of a pharmacist's education, you have to break down the complex concepts you learned in school into layman's terms. The majority of your day will be spent teaching others about their medications, insurance, and how the pharmacy industry works.

Empathy

Anyone who walks into a pharmacy probably has a question regarding their medication or pharmacy insurance. Sometimes, you'll meet people who are sick, in a bad mood, and want their medications as soon as possible. You may have to deal with unpleasant people occasionally, which is why having empathy is very important because you are able to understand their frustrations and communicate with them better. If you think you lack empathy or have trouble expressing empathy, not to worry, these are skills that you can learn.

Passion for Helping Others

Most people you meet at the pharmacy will be polite, but some people will be in pain, annoyed, sick, and simply not the best version of themselves at that moment. There will be moments when your passion to help others outweighs situations when you're dealing with a difficult patient. Don't forget about your team of pharmacy technicians, cashiers, nurses, and doctors. You, the pharmacist, are there to help them do their jobs better. Doctors and nurses will often ask your advice on medications. Pharmacy technicians and cashiers will look to you for guidance in order to keep the pharmacy running as smoothly as possible. It will be your passion that drives you not just to help your patients but to help everyone in the pharmacy.

Lifelong Learner

Pharmacy school teaches you the most up-to-date concepts for the period of time that you are a student. New drugs get approved and changes to older medications occur every year and you will need to update your knowledge to keep yourself current. You will never be bored with pharmacy because there's a wealth of medication news, fascinating research, and new drug approvals that you can always read up on. You'll always be learning something new at your job and that makes pharmacy interesting, unlike some other professions (*cough* accounting).

And I have good news, doing all the above, you typically earn a six-figure base salary when hired right out of pharmacy school. If you are curious about the exact salary average, flip to the *How Much Does a Pharmacist Make*? section, which is conveniently sorted by state and pharmacy industry.

If you want to analyze your personality on a deeper level, I highly recommend this strangely accurate and free online test. Visit https://www.16personalities.com/

Reasons to be a Pharmacist

According to the American Association of College of Pharmacy, these are the top 10 reasons people want to become pharmacists[1]:

1. They want to help people get well
2. They like to work directly with patients
3. They enjoy a wide variety of career opportunities
4. They can benefit from the demand for pharmacists
5. They want to be an important member of the healthcare team
6. They can have job mobility, stability, and flexibility
7. They are excited to be a part of major innovations in medication therapy
8. They want to work with state-of-the-art technology
9. They can help defend against bioterrorism
10. They would like to be a highly respected member of their community

Reasons NOT to be a Pharmacist

Just as there are many benefits of becoming a pharmacist, there are also many drawbacks to pursuing this profession. Below are the seven common reasons that make people think twice about pursuing a PharmD.

1. **Huge financial investment:** According to the 2018 survey conducted by the American Association of Colleges of Pharmacy [2], the average amount borrowed to finance a PharmD degree is $193,396 for students who attend a private institution and $137,356 for those who attend public colleges. Note that these amounts do not include undergraduate student debt, which averaged $37,172 in 2016[3].
2. **Not enough respect:** Pharmacists, in general, do not receive the same kind of respect (as physicians) from their patients. There are people who are not aware of the fact that pharmacists do hold a doctorate degree and treat them simply as pill counters. Even for those who are aware, it is not uncommon to see them yelling at their retail pharmacists for taking too long to get their medications ready.
3. **Rigorous training:** It usually takes three to four years of intensive education and training after college to become a pharmacist. Long hours of study, preparing for examinations on a regular basis can be overwhelming at times.
4. **Great responsibility:** A pharmacist's responsibility goes beyond handing over the medication to the patient. An error in medication verification, for example, could potentially kill a patient resulting in big fine or even jail time (thus permanent loss of license to practice) for the pharmacist.

5. **Physically straining:** Most retail pharmacists are required to stand on their feet the entire time at work; the work shift can be as long as twelve hours. There is also a considerable amount of reaching and bending during the prescription-filling process. The physical requirement can be a turn-off for some people.
6. **Job security:** The healthcare industry is constantly changing and that means the security of a pharmacist's job is not the same as it used to be. The cut in federal funding for Medicare, for example, resulted in hundreds of hospital closures across the nation. The increased usage of robots in pharmacy has also lowered the demand for pharmacists in certain settings.
7. **High barrier to entry:** Getting into a pharmacy school is increasingly challenging. The competition is fierce as the number of applicants to pharmacy school increases each year and the popularity of the pharmacy profession is rising (despite all the negative aspects discussed above).

After reading the aforementioned negative aspects of pursuing the pharmacy profession, perhaps some may feel pharmacy is not for them. Below are the exact same points with a different perspective:

1. **Huge financial investment:** Many people overlook the huge financial return as a result of the investment. According to the U.S. Census Bureau, only 5.4% of Americans in 2018 make a six-figure income or greater. That means you, as a pharmacist, will be making more than 94.6 percent of the remaining population! The high earning potential is but one perk of being a pharmacist. The benefits and opportunities in the pharmacy profession are only limited by your imagination.
2. **Not enough respect:** It takes time and effort to earn respect.

This applies to individuals who spend a certain amount of time interacting with you at your job such as doctors, nurses, and fellow pharmacists. Also, take a look at whether you are confusing respect with other things such as acceptance, affirmation, and praise. There will always be people in our society who will disrespect you no matter how well you treat them. If you are doing the right thing to the best of your ability/knowledge, you should feel good about yourself.

3. **Rigorous training:** Nothing worthwhile comes easy. The same principle applies to the value we provide to our society: we can contribute more when we become more or highly skilled in certain areas (pharmacy in this case). If you like the idea of being a valuable member of society, take your training and education seriously. If it was easy to become a pharmacist, everyone would be doing it.

4. **Great responsibility:** If we cannot handle critical matters, we won't be given any major responsibilities. Great responsibilities come with great power, which usually means greater impact on others' lives as well as higher earning potential.

5. **Physically straining:** Growth happens on the other side of suffering and we won't know how strong we are until being strong is the only option. With training and practice, we can become stronger! Being on your feet is more beneficial than sitting. Standing can lower your risk of stroke, keep you at a healthier weight, and increase muscle tone in your legs, core, and back. The twelve-hour shift is voluntary, not mandatory. Besides that, there are pharmacists who work from home where no standing is required. Also, in offices and in hospitals there are plenty of chairs to sit on.

6. **Job security:** Today, change is the only constant, nothing is ever

secure. And if making more than 94.6 percent of the remaining population doesn't give you a sense of security, we really don't know what would. The profession of pharmacy will continue to evolve to become more specialized. As long as there are new medications being made and people are getting older, there is always a demand for pharmacists.

7. **High barrier to entry**: The only barrier we have is the one we set for ourselves, commonly known as self-imposed limitation. People tend to talk themselves out of trying difficult tasks to avoid the pain of failure or rather harsh criticism from others. "Often, the journey to greatness begins the moment our preference for comfort and certainty are overruled by a greater purpose that requires challenge and contributions" – Brendon Burchard. Getting into pharmacy school is definitely a challenge; going through the training won't be easy and securing your ideal pharmacy job usually requires overcoming your own fears of rejection (this is an area where networking is very beneficial). It seems like there are high barriers to achieving anything of great value. However, if other people can do it, so can you! If there is a will, there is always a way, or so they say.

There are pros and cons to any profession. We're sharing with you our experiences, the good and the bad, so you can make a well-informed decision. We can focus on the negatives and be convinced of our inadequacy or we can focus on the positives and keep striving towards the dreams we desire (becoming a pharmacist) and deserve. We achieve whatever we focus on.

Is the Pharmacist Job Market Too Saturated?

Worry #1: "Ahh! We're being replaced by automated pill-filling machines!"

First of all, counting pills is just the tip of the iceberg in terms of a pharmacist's responsibilities. Drugs come in many forms—oral, topical, sublingual, rectal, etc. Pharmacists manage all of these formulations. Other healthcare-related functions include monitoring patients for adverse drug reactions, drug-drug interactions and drug-food interactions. They also provide counseling services for doctors, nurses, and patients. A robot will never measure up to a warm-blooded pharmacist. It's like comparing an electronic mixer to a baker; the mixer helps speed up the dough-making process but it can't bake a delicious loaf of banana bread on its own.

You can learn more about numerous career opportunities in Chapter 3, *What Can I Do with a PharmD?*

Worry #2: "Will I be able to find a job after getting a PharmD?"

You might be wondering whether pharmacy is the right career choice for you and whether it is still worth pursuing, especially now that the market is "saturated". In a world where new pharmacy schools are popping up like daisies, this is a valid concern. Rather than panicking, let's take a look at the Pharmacist Demand Index (PDI). The PDI reflects the demand for pharmacists and is measured on a scale of 1 to 5, where 5 stands for the highest demand for pharmacists, 3 stands for a balance in supply of pharmacists and corresponding demand, and a 1 stands for no demand. In the third quarter of 2018, the population-adjusted PDI in the United States in general is 3.17. PDI is also location-specific. Regions in the United States with higher PDIs are the West at 3.4, the Northeast at 3.21 and the Midwest at 3.14, whereas the South has the lowest PDI of 2.91[4]. While there may be some saturation in several southern regions, you'll find plenty of opportunities elsewhere.

As more and more baby boomers turn 65 years old (2011–2029), the demand for pharmacists to serve the elderly will continue to increase year by year. In fact, the demand for pharmacists to take on additional roles and responsibilities has increased so much that the Senate Bill 493 was passed in October 2013. Senate Bill 493 allows pharmacists to obtain the advanced practice qualifications needed to serve the increasing healthcare needs of society. These advanced pharmacists can perform a range of new functions from ordering and interpreting drug therapy-related tests to evaluating and managing the patient's well-being in collaboration with other healthcare providers.[5] An Advanced Practice Pharmacist (APh) may also initiate, adjust, and discontinue a drug therapy while working with a physician. The field of pharmacy will continue to evolve, and pharmacists will continue to join forces with other healthcare professionals.

If Rome could be built in a day, there would be a lot of Romes in the world. Becoming a pharmacist is similar—no one becomes a pharmacist without studying for five to eight years and certainly not without taking licensing exams. Not every Tom, Dick, and Henrietta can become a pharmacist. As a pharmacist, you will have very specialized knowledge and skill sets.

Worry #3: "Ugh! While in pharmacy school, I worked as a pharmacy intern but didn't get hired on as a pharmacist after I graduated."

The good news is that this is something you can influence. Most pharmacies are looking to hire interns as pharmacists. Make a good impression by arriving to work early and working hard. If you don't have anything to do, ask how you can help. Ask questions. Be engaged. You'll get an offer.

About twenty years ago, when pharmacists were in shortage, even the worst pharmacists were offered a sign-on bonus. Yes, those days are over and perhaps for the benefit of the patients. The profession of pharmacy is now a normal job where you have to present yourself professionally; know how to market yourself in order to get hired. Do your due diligence and you will succeed.

By the way, there are some pharmacies that just exploit interns as free labor, but let's face it; you wouldn't want to work there anyway. Run, don't walk, away from those pharmacies!

Worries #4, 5, and 6: "I heard more and more pharmacists are desperate to take on any job as there are less pharmacist jobs in the market. There seem to be way more applicants than the number of available positions in any pharmacy company. There is a lot of competition! How can I maximize my chance of getting hired? And how do I avoid getting underpaid? Is it possible that pharmacists' salaries may decrease?"

Suck it up and stop complaining. Next question.

3

WHAT CAN I DO WITH A PHARMD?

"There exist limitless opportunities in every industry. Where there is an open mind, there will always be a frontier." – Charles Kettering

WITH A PHARMD DEGREE, your career opportunities are only limited by your own imagination. Just think about the number of different disease states or illnesses that inflict human health, you will then realize how valuable medication knowledge can be. Being a medication expert, your advice is not only respected but is also highly appreciated by your patients as your advice could mean the difference between life and death.[1] For example, a severe allergic reaction (hives) can be resolved by an over-the-counter medication, Benadryl. You also saved them a trip to the local clinic and several hours of panic and worry.

In this section, we will go over the career options you can choose from with a PharmD degree. Knowing about the various opportunities will make you a well-informed and therefore stronger pharmacy school applicant, especially during the interview.

Community Pharmacy

Community pharmacists are typically the first line of healthcare.[2] They are highly accessible to the public; patients do not need an appointment to be able to speak with a pharmacist for advice. This is highly impactful, especially in low-income communities where people cannot afford to see a doctor or seek alternative therapy to an expensive medication prescribed to them. Community pharmacists are also the last line of defense as they are the ones doing the final medication verification before it gets to the patient's hand. In addition to dispensing medications, monitoring patients for adverse drug reactions, drug-drug and drug-food interactions, pharmacists also provide counseling services, such as over-the-counter medication recommendation and referral to other healthcare specialties. It is very common to see pharmacists who enjoy patient interactions in community settings open their own independent or compounding pharmacies, so they can personalize their service to serve the needs of the community. Another option is to work in retail chains such as CVS Pharmacy, Walgreens, Rite Aid, etc.

Compounding/Independent Pharmacy

An independent pharmacy is a community pharmacy that is not a retail chain. You have the option to own or work in an independent pharmacy, and they are usually run by a pharmacist rather than a big corporation. The majority of independent pharmacies have a compounding pharmacy service. A compounding pharmacist practices in preparing new forms of medication. For example, if there are only tablets available for a certain medication, a compounding pharmacist can make a lollipop for the patient to suck on or an oral solution to help the patient swallow better. There are many drug products being removed from the market as a result of economic reasons rather than safety concerns. This loss of manufactured medications is made up in part by compounding pharmacists when physicians prescribe a medication that is no longer available.

Compounding pharmacies also cater to special patient populations such as women who need bioidentical hormone replacement therapy, geriatrics for pain management, pediatrics for personalized medication dosage forms, people with sports injuries, and dental patients.

Compounding pharmacy is not only reserved for humans but expands to veterinary patients (dogs, cats, birds, reptiles, livestock, exotics, etc.). Veterinary pharmacy is a small but growing area of interest for pharmacists. If you are a strong, business-minded individual who wants to open and run your own business, help patients (human and non-human), and share medical knowledge, starting an independent pharmacy could be your calling. The mission to educate and inform patients about their medications and how to live healthier lifestyles has been the foundation of a thriving independent pharmacy business. [3]

Hospital Pharmacy

To work in a hospital pharmacy setting, one or two years of residency experience is highly recommended (sometimes required) in addition to pharmacy school. Hospital pharmacists focus on utilizing their drug knowledge without the need to handle any insurance issues or customer complaints that are commonly encountered in the community pharmacy settings. In this area, pharmacists are heavily involved in patient care; they monitor patient progress and adjust patient medications for optimal outcome, order laboratory tests such as the basic metabolic panel (BMP), comprehensive metabolic panel (CMP), and liver function tests. They work very closely with physicians, nutritionists, nurses, and other healthcare professionals to determine the most appropriate and effective drug regimen for the patient.[4] Hospital pharmacists can also further specialize in a variety of concentrations such as critical care, surgery, cardiology, pediatrics, neurology, infectious diseases, drug information, psychiatric pharmacy, and transition care.

Ambulatory Care Pharmacy

Pharmacists play an integral role in the healthcare team in clinical sites with regard to optimizing patient outcomes and cost-effectiveness of medication usage. Pharmacists take on increasing responsibility in medication therapy management for patients with high blood pressure, diabetes, chronic obstructive pulmonary disease (COPD), asthma, and other chronic diseases. They often prescribe medication, order labs and work closely with the patient and collaborate with their physicians. Amcare pharmacists help patients achieve desired treatment outcomes through proper management of their medications and educate them about healthy diet and lifestyle choices. [5]

Geriatric Pharmacy/Consultant Pharmacist

Geriatric pharmacists, commonly known as consultant pharmacists, focus on counseling older patients regarding their medications. If you were to poke your head in your grandmother's medicine cabinet, you may see bottles of medications. Older patients tend to take a variety of medications to help manage their chronic conditions such as pain, hypertension, high cholesterol, arthritis, coronary heart disease, diabetes, chronic kidney disease, heart failure, depression, Alzheimer's disease, and chronic obstructive pulmonary disease (COPD). In addition, this category of patients is also more prone to flus and infections. [6]

Geriatric pharmacists are usually found working in skilled nursing facilities (SNF), assisted living facilities, and hospice facilities. A geriatric pharmacist's main role in these settings is medication therapy management (MTM) where the pharmacist manages patients' medications and speaks with patients about when and how to take the medications, potential side effects, and how to separate medications so as to avoid potential drug-drug interactions and monitor adverse drug reactions. They frequently make recommendations on medication dosage adjustment or medication replacement to reduce unwanted side effects. They conduct routine tests such as blood sugar and blood pressure monitoring. Based on the results, these pharmacists change or switch medications for the patients and address any concerns or questions the patients' might have about their medications.

Geriatric patients usually take a lot more medications compared to younger adults and therefore there are more drug-drug interactions to be concerned about. Geriatric pharmacists are highly trained in how to handle these issues to prevent major adverse drug reactions. Older patients are also physiologically more sensitive to certain medications that put them at greater risk of falling, which could potentially lead to a hip fracture. These pharmacists are constantly educating patients and their caregivers about high-risk medications and how to reduce risks while being on these medications.

Governmental Agencies

Finding work in this area is possibly the least well-known career option among most pharmacy students. Surprisingly, there are many opportunities in the government sector such as the Public Health Service, Food and Drug Administration (FDA), the Veterans Administration (VA), the National Institutes of Health, county hospitals, state prisons and the armed forces. In the military (Navy, Air Force, Army) pharmacists are not only responsible for compounding and dispensing prescriptions, but they also supervise military and civilian pharmacy personnel. (Note that pharmacists who service the Marine Corp are most likely to be Navy) They screen prescriptions for proper interpretation and dosages and advise patients and nurses of the standard dosage regimen, side effects, storage requirements, and any special instructions. Like other clinical pharmacists, they monitor patients' drug therapy and advise other pharmacists and the medical staff on the characteristics of the drug, dosages, indications, contraindications, and availability of medications.

At first glance, the salary may not look very appealing; however, the employee benefits make up for that. The best perk is the public service loan forgiveness program where you make 120 qualifying payments (which equates to 10 years) and get the remaining balance forgiven. Keep in mind you may owe a lot of money after finishing pharmacy school; therefore, this forgiveness program is an awesome deal. Not to mention, federal employees have excellent healthcare benefits including a nationally recognized model offering 200+ health plan options throughout the U.S., no waiting period or physical examination to enroll, no exclusions for pre-existing conditions, substantial employer contribution to premiums (up to 75%), option to pay premiums with pretax dollars, coverage for self and eligible family members, opportunity to retain coverage into retirement with full government contributions, and the opportunity to continue coverage for dependents.

On top of the incredible medical benefits, they also enjoy amazing leave and holiday benefits, which include 10 paid holidays, 13 days of sick leave with no carryover ceiling, and accrue 13, 20 or 26 days of vacation leave depending upon years of service or related work experience. Pharmacists in the Navy can also carry up to 30 days of vacation leave into the next calendar year and take family and medical leave of absence for up to 12 weeks per year of unpaid leave. Another rare benefit includes up to 104 hours of paid leave for disabled veterans during their first year of employment for purposes of undergoing medical treatment for such disability. [7]

Other great benefits include:

- Dental and Vision Insurance Programs
- Flexible Spending Accounts
- Long-Term Care Insurance Program
- Federal Employees Group Life Insurance Program
- Federal Employees Retirement System (FERS)
- Thrift Savings Plan (like a civilian 401k retirement plan)
- Work/Life Programs
    - Alternative Work Schedules – shifts other than the traditional eight-hour days/40-hour weeks are available
    - Telework – activities may authorize employees in eligible positions to perform some duties from home or a telecommuting center
    - Part-time Employment/Job Sharing
    - Leave Sharing Programs – allow coworkers to transfer leave to others in need
    - Transportation Subsidy – employees taking public transportation/carpools are reimbursed for transportation costs
    - Health & Fitness – many Navy/Marine Corps installations have well-equipped fitness centers available to civilian employees
    - Dependent Care – the Navy has outstanding child care programs and referrals to Federal child care centers
    - Tuition Reimbursement – activities may pay all or part of the necessary expenses of training, including the costs of college tuition for training and education, to improve an employee's performance of his or her official duties
    - Student Loan Repayment Program – activities may repay student loans up to annual limits
    - Employee Assistance Programs

More details can be found in these links below:

Navy Benefits (https://bit.ly/2EvFAec)

Air Force Benefits for Pharmacist (https://bit.ly/24CkjEQ)

Army Benefits for Pharmacists (https://bit.ly/2jNobSH)

If you do not want to join the military but want to reap all the military benefits, you can consider the US Health Public Service where you can work as a commissioned officer. You are subject to physical training exams similar to military standards. There is a huge network of duty stations (another term for place of work) where you can apply for assignments all over the US.

Home Healthcare

Pharmacists also work with patients in their homes and other residential facilities such as assisted living communities. Most of the prescription orders written by physicians are intravenous (IV) admixture, which is prepared by the home healthcare pharmacists. They also prepare pain management medication, nutritional supplements and chemotherapy. Pharmacists also monitor their patients' progress and adjust therapy as needed.[8] Due to the complex nature of the compounded medications as well as the setup requirement, home healthcare pharmacies typically service a small patient population of about 50 to 80 at a time. Pharmacists in this specialty tend to partner with hospice organizations, visiting nurses, and social service organizations. Home healthcare pharmacists' daily duties include inpatient care services, medication dispensing and counseling, business management, medication preparation, and health professional counseling.

Managed Care

Managed care organizations consist of health plans, pharmacy benefit management (PBM) companies, integrated delivery networks (IDNs), and accountable care organizations (ACOs). Pharmacists in these settings play important roles in the delivery of prescription drug benefits to over 270 million Americans in a cost-effective manner. Drug therapy optimization, drug formulary development, therapeutic protocol evaluation, patient consultation, and reduction in unnecessary doctor visits and hospitalization are all examples of cost-effective measures and responsibilities of pharmacists who practice in the managed care environment.[9] Preventive care is one of the main areas of emphasis in the managed care world since the cost of treating an illness usually outweighs the cost of preventing it from happening.

There are about 20,000 pharmacists currently working for health plans and pharmacy benefit management companies in the United States. As these entities gain popularity for reducing patients' healthcare expenses, there is an increasing need for pharmacists and other healthcare professionals to serve patients through these organizations.

Managed care pharmacists and other healthcare professionals provide a range of services that seek to ensure that patients—namely individuals served by a health plan or an ACO or IDN—receive appropriate medication therapies conveniently and cost effectively. Pharmacists must possess both clinical skills and the ability to evaluate scientific evidence and apply these principles to enhance patient and population health outcome while optimizing healthcare resources.

Managed care pharmacists also design pharmacy benefits for health plans, communicate and collaborate with patients, prescribers, and other pharmacists, and institute practices and processes that detect unsafe medicines to ensure patient safety. All these practices help to ensure that all patients have access to the medications they need in an efficient and cost-effective way.

Pharmaceutical Industry

The pharmaceutical industry offers many opportunities for pharmacists in research and development, sales/marketing and business development.[10] Because pharmacists have a deep understanding of pharmacology, there are many opportunities such as working with medical information, making improvements in pharmaceutical formulation, quality assurance, and regulatory affairs.

Pharmacy in Academia

The three pillars of academia are: teaching, scholarship, and service.[11] Pharmacists in academia play the key role of educating and inspiring future pharmacists. Academia is an attractive option not only for those who enjoy working with students but also for pharmacists who like to engage in clinical practice, evidence-based and peer-review research.[12] Advanced degrees like MA/MS/MBA/PhD certification and/or 1 to 2 years of residency or fellowship experiences are recommended for this field.

Academic pharmacists are not confined to the conventional laboratory or classroom environment. They work with other healthcare professionals to select or design optimal medication regimens for patients. Many are involved with medication therapy management services offered by companies like Mirixa and OutcomesMTM, providing individualized medication counseling to improve medication therapeutic outcomes as well as to reduce healthcare costs.

In academia, pharmacists work at the college of pharmacy in addition to other healthcare-related institutions. Positions range from the dean of a pharmacy school to a teaching clinical pharmacy position at an off-campus site or to a classroom setting. Responsibilities include administrative functions, scientific research, teaching professional student pharmacists, supervising research and teaching graduate students, speaking and/or publishing in scientific venues, student advising, and mentoring student pharmacists through experiential practice sites.

Nuclear Pharmacy

Established in 1978 by the Board of Pharmaceutical Specialties, nuclear pharmacy is a specialty department that requires pharmacists to prepare radioactive materials/medications that are used in the diagnosis or treatment of specific illnesses.[13] Nuclear pharmacists must undergo extensive training in radiation safety with regard to preparing, compounding, and delivery of radioactive materials. The two main sites where nuclear pharmacists work are: (1) Institutional nuclear pharmacy that is commonly linked to a hospital or medical center and (2) Commercial nuclear pharmacy that is centrally located near many clinics or hospitals. While the preparation of radiopharmaceuticals is carried out on site at the first setting, the second location requires additional transportation of radioactive materials to be made in a timely fashion.

Nuclear pharmacists play a vital role in the provision of nuclear medicine services. To ensure proper administration of radiopharmaceutical products, nuclear pharmacists must clearly communicate with nuclear medicine personnel on how to prepare the patients prior to giving or injecting radioactive drugs. Unexpected outcomes can sometimes occur; nuclear pharmacists must be ready to troubleshoot problems on site and offer solutions. This is why it is critical for nuclear pharmacists to perform functional checks for their equipment and devices and to determine and document the quality and purity of each radiopharmaceutical.

Mail Order Pharmacy

With an increased number of third-party insurance organizations and the expansion of internet pharmacy services, mail order pharmacy is doing more than just the conventional medication dispensing function. Today's mail service pharmacists are involved in patient care and overall patient satisfaction. Their duties include medication counseling and other patient care services such as disease management and medication therapy management. Pillpack (currently owned by Amazon) is one of the most popular mail order pharmacies, which provides 24/7 support via phone, text, email or live chat for patients who have any questions related to their medications.[14]

A mail service pharmacy helps patients reduce their overall healthcare costs in terms of lower co-payments for an extended supply of medication (up to three months). Patients save on transportation expenses as they no longer have to make multiple trips per year to the local pharmacy store. No more waiting in line or chasing refills from doctors! Transportation to a physical pharmacy could be a real hassle for elderly people or their family members. This is why mail order pharmacies will remain relevant for many years to come.

What mail service pharmacists enjoy most about this career option is that they can focus on patient care and satisfaction. The counseling aspect of the job also gives pharmacists the feeling of satisfaction, knowing that they are helping people and saving lives every single day.

Other Specialties

As the pharmacy profession evolves, there is an increasing demand for pharmacists who specialize in legal practice, health administration, business management, consulting, marketing, drug information, veterinary care, poison control, etc. In essence, the market always looks for those who can adapt to the changing landscape or nature of the pharmacy industry. More pharmacy schools are now offering a range of dual and joint degrees in combination with a PharmD to better prepare students for the increasing demand of the market.

4

HOW DO I CHOOSE WHICH PHARMACY SCHOOL TO APPLY TO?

"It is in your moments of decision that your destiny is shaped." – Tony Robbins

WITH OVER 140 PHARMACY schools across the United States, choosing which one to apply to can be a daunting task. Luckily, you are reading this book and we've been through the whole process. Below are important factors to keep in mind when considering perspective pharmacy schools.

What are your goals as a pharmacist?

If you have no clue what your goals are as a pharmacist and all you're focused on is getting into pharmacy school, that's okay! The best advice we can give you is to keep all your options open. Keep in mind that there are a lot of different things you can do as a pharmacist, from retail to hospital, research to opening your own business. If you have a general idea which areas of pharmacy interest you, that's a good place to start as certain pharmacy schools will have more opportunities and emphasis on particular areas such as research, clinical or community. That way, when searching for which pharmacy school to apply to, you will be applying to pharmacy schools that align with your life goals.

What are your goals in terms of time? Most pharmacy schools have a standard four-year PharmD degree program, but there are three-year pharmacy degree programs, dual degrees, and even accelerated programs for students who graduated from high school. Do you want to be a pharmacist with a business degree? What about a pharmacist with a law degree? Dual degrees are programs that allow you to earn a doctorate degree in pharmacy while obtaining another degree such as a Master of Science (M.S.), Doctor of Philosophy (Ph.D.), Master of Business Administration (M.B.A.), Master of Public Health (M.P.H.), Juris Doctor (J.D.) or Doctor of Medicine (M.D.). Click here for a list of dual degree programs[1]. Keep in mind that for dual degree programs additional standardized exams may be required. For accelerated programs for high school students, refer to Chapter 6 *Accelerated Pharmacy Programs.* You have so many options on various graduate programs related to a PharmD. Bet you weren't expecting that!

Pharmacy schools are all designed to give you the knowledge needed as a pharmacist to pass your board exam. Keep in mind that not all pharmacy schools are created equal. Some have better teaching programs that help you better prepare for your licensure exams while others, well, let's just say they may need some room for improvement. Therefore, it is very important to check out the pass rates for the licensing exam called NAPLEX (North American Pharmacist Licensure Examination) for your school of interest. In our opinion, a licensure pass rate of 85% or above is decent. Click licensure pass rates[2] to look up each of the pharmacy school's pass rates.

Where do you want to live?

Almost each state in the United States has a pharmacy school. Your options range from attending a school close to home or exploring an entirely new city. Go to www.aacp.org/resources/school-locator to see a pharmacy school locator interactive map[3]. Keep in mind that most of your networking will take place around the school you eventually go to. For example, if you attend a pharmacy school in Southern California, most of your internship and rotation opportunities will be focused around that area, which could lead to a job opportunity after graduation. Don't worry; this isn't a hard limit. Many students attend schools in one location then relocate to a different place to work. There are many regional and national pharmacy events that you can attend. Having a pharmacy degree allows you to have the mobility to work anywhere in the country.

How competitive are you as an applicant?

Your level of competitiveness is mainly based on your science, prerequisite, and overall GPA. Basically, the higher your GPA the more options you will have. Refer to the GPA section in Chapter 7 for appropriate strategies according to your stats. The table with the average admitted students' GPA (sorted in ascending order) will allow you to gauge your likelihood of getting accepted at different schools.

How much do you want to pay?

This is probably the most neglected topic among college students who are overly concerned about getting into a pharmacy program. Pharmacy schools vary in the amount of tuition from about 100k to 200k for the whole program and the prices keep going up! We will go into detail about real dollar amount costs for a PharmD degree. The next chapter includes a table that lists all the out-of-state tuition costs for all the pharmacy schools so make sure you flip through that section!

When we were in your shoes, tuition cost was the least of our worries because the most important thing is getting in, right? Wrong! Tuition costs should be one of your top factors when considering which pharmacy schools to apply to. The lower the tuition the better off you will be when you graduate, especially when you factor in high interest rates. Of course, the perfect blend would be a low-tuition pharmacy school located in a good area with decent licensure passing scores.

We are saving you from many years of painful, endless payments to your student loan. When time travel is possible, you best believe we're going back in time to hand this book to our younger selves.

5

HOW MUCH DOES A PHARMD DEGREE COST?

"An investment in knowledge pays the best interest." – Benjamin Franklin

UNDERESTIMATING THE COST OF getting a PharmD is a common mistake that prospective pharmacists make. They're so concerned about getting in that they lose sight of what it actually costs to get the degree. There is nothing quite like the student loan cloud of doom looming over your head as you attempt to save for retirement. We'll be calculating the actual cost of pharmacy school education and potentially save you from that fate (or at least shrink that intimidating cloud). This section contains tips on how to reduce the loan amount as well as to pay it off faster.

Attending a public college, versus a private one, in your state of residence is generally less expensive. We highly recommend public colleges if possible. In 2018, students who graduated from private institutions borrowed an average of $193,396 compared to the $137,356 borrowed by those graduating from public schools. When you factor in that these numbers are just the average loan amounts and not the cumulative amount of the expenses that you will encounter during your pursuit of a PharmD, choosing the right college is a crucial first step.

In the United States, public pharmacy schools are generally limited to one or two per state, so tuition should be relatively easy to research independently. We have included tuition costs for both public and private schools but only the out-of-state tuition rate in the two tables below for your reference.

Table 1 shows schools sorted by state and Table 2 shows schools sorted by total tuition and fees. Costs of living are not included in the table as they vary greatly from one individual to another and can be estimated to be $20,000 plus or minus $5,000 per year.

Cost of Tuition 2018-2019

Table 1: PharmD Tuition Sorted by Location

State	Pharmacy School	Year 1	Year 2	Year 3	Year 4	Total
AL	Auburn University	$41,108	$43,163	$45,322	$47,588	$177,181
AL	Samford University	$47,826	$50,217	$52,728	$55,365	$206,136
AR	Harding University	$39,030	$40,982	$43,031	$45,182	$168,224
AR	University of Arkansas	$42,806	$44,946	$47,194	$49,553	$184,499
AZ	University of Arizona	$47,060	$49,413	$51,884	$54,478	$202,834
AZ	Midwestern University - Glendale Campus	$45,909	$48,204	$50,615	$53,145	$197,874
CA	West Coast University	$43,780	$45,969	$48,267	$50,681	$188,697
CA	California Northstate University	$49,520	$49,310	$49,638	$48,910	$197,378
CA	California Health Sciences University	$45,605	$47,885	$50,280	$52,793	$196,563
CA	University of the Pacific	$79,148	$79,148	$52,772		$211,068
CA	Keck Graduate Institute	$46,900	$49,245	$51,707	$54,293	$202,145
CA	Loma Linda University	$47,364	$49,732	$52,219	$54,830	$204,145
CA	Touro University California	$47,200	$49,560	$52,038	$54,640	$203,438
CA	Western University of Health Sciences	$49,725	$49,725	$49,725	$50,075	$199,250
CA	University of California, San Francisco	$63,809	$63,809	$63,809		$191,427
CA	Chapman University	$69,750	$69,750	$46,500		$186,000
CA	Marshall B. Ketchum University	$49,430	$51,902	$54,497	$57,221	$213,049
CA	University of California, San Diego	$40,427	$40,327	$44,432	$40,327	$165,513
CA	University of Southern California	$56,846	$56,846	$56,846	$56,846	$227,384
CO	Regis University	$36,460	$38,283	$40,197	$42,207	$157,147

State	Pharmacy School	Year 1	Year 2	Year 3	Year 4	Total
CO	University of Colorado	$39,870	$41,864	$43,957	$46,155	$171,845
CT	University of Connecticut	$36,948	$38,795	$53,552	$56,230	$185,525
CT	University of Saint Joseph	$50,569	$53,097	$55,752	$58,540	$217,959
DC	Howard University	$28,000	$29,400	$30,870	$32,414	$120,684
FL	University of Florida	$36,000	$37,800	$39,690	$41,675	$155,165
FL	Lake Erie College of Osteopathic Medicine - Bradenton Campus	$32,113	$33,719	$35,405	$37,175	$138,411
FL	Larkin University	$45,492	$45,492	$46,715		$137,699
FL	Florida A&M University	$36,566	$38,394	$40,314	$42,330	$157,604
FL	Nova Southeastern University	$38,425	$40,346	$42,364	$44,482	$165,617
FL	Palm Beach Atlantic University	$37,800	$37,800	$37,800	$25,864	$139,264
FL	University of South Florida	$36,000	$37,800	$39,690	$41,675	$155,165
GA	Philadelphia College of Osteopathic Medicine - Georgia Campus	$41,538	$41,538	$41,538	$41,538	$166,152
GA	Mercer University	$30,000	$35,000	$35,000	$40,000	$140,000
GA	University of Georgia	$36,850	$41,458	$36,850	$36,850	$152,008
GA	South University (GA)	$36,972	$38,821	$40,762	$42,800	$159,354
HI	University of Hawaii at Hilo	$41,248	$41,498	$41,738	$41,978	$166,462
IA	The University of Iowa	$44,790	$47,030	$49,381	$51,850	$193,051
IA	Drake University	$40,572	$40,572	$40,572	$45,662	$167,378
ID	Idaho State University	$38,312	$40,228	$42,239	$44,351	$165,130
IL	Chicago State University	$39,410	$41,381	$43,450	$45,622	$169,862
IL	Midwestern University - Downers Grove Campus	$45,909	$48,204	$50,615	$53,145	$197,874

State	Pharmacy School	Year 1	Year 2	Year 3	Year 4	Total
IL	Roosevelt University	$50,902	$53,447	$56,119	$58,925	$219,394
IL	Rosalind Franklin University of Medicine and Science	$36,463	$38,286	$40,200	$42,210	$157,160
IL	University of Illinois at Chicago	$44,799	$47,039	$49,391	$51,860	$193,089
IL	Southern Illinois University	$31,894	$33,489	$35,163	$36,921	$137,467
IN	Manchester University	$39,780	$41,769	$43,857	$46,050	$171,457
IN	Butler University	$42,790	$42,790	$42,790	$46,590	$174,960
IN	Purdue University	$40,276	$42,290	$44,404	$46,625	$173,595
KS	The University of Kansas	$41,480	$43,554	$45,732	$48,018	$178,784
KY	University of Kentucky	$50,665	$53,198	$55,858	$58,651	$218,372
KY	Sullivan University	$56,620	$59,451	$62,424		$178,495
LA	The University of Louisiana Monroe	$43,718	$45,904	$48,199	$50,609	$188,430
LA	Xavier University of Louisiana	$33,640	$35,322	$37,088	$38,943	$144,993
Lebanon	Lebanese American University	$25,620	$26,901	$28,246	$29,658	$110,425
MA	Massachusetts College of Pharmacy and Health Sciences - Worcester	$51,600	$54,180	$56,889		$162,669
MA	Massachusetts College of Pharmacy and Health Sciences - Boston	$32,600	$38,300	$40,215	$42,226	$153,341
MA	Northeastern University	$47,720	$50,106	$52,611	$55,242	$205,679
MA	Western New England University	$43,596	$45,776	$48,065	$50,468	$187,904
MD	Notre Dame of Maryland University	$38,750	$40,688	$42,722	$44,858	$167,017
MD	University of Maryland	$44,900	$47,145	$49,502	$51,977	$193,525
MD	University of Maryland	$60,135	$63,142	$66,299	$69,614	$259,189
ME	University of New England	$42,805	$44,945	$47,193	$49,552	$184,495

State	Pharmacy School	Year 1	Year 2	Year 3	Year 4	Total
ME	Husson University	$37,074	$35,070	$42,084	$31,062	$145,290
MI	Ferris State University	$23,000	$24,150	$25,358	$26,625	$99,133
MI	Wayne State University	$51,063	$55,764	$46,056	$44,489	$197,372
MI	University of Michigan	$36,666	$36,666	$36,666	$54,999	$164,997
MN	University of Minnesota	$41,666	$41,666	$43,749	$45,937	$173,018
MO	University of Missouri	$51,476	$54,050	$56,752	$59,590	$221,868
MS	William Carey University	$40,000	$42,000	$44,100	$46,305	$172,405
MS	The University of Mississippi	$48,534	$48,534	$52,072	$52,072	$201,212
MT	University of Montana	$30,190	$31,700	$33,284	$34,949	$130,123
NC	Campbell University	$39,200	$39,200	$39,200	$39,200	$156,800
NC	The University of North Carolina (UNC) at Chapel Hill Eshelman	$51,894	$45,356	$51,894	$45,356	$194,500
NC	High Point University	$40,522	$42,548	$44,676	$46,909	$174,655
NC	Wingate University - Hendersonville, NC	$33,244	$34,906	$36,652	$38,484	$143,286
NC	Wingate University - Wingate, NC	$33,244	$34,906	$36,652	$38,484	$143,286
ND	North Dakota State University	$23,614	$24,795	$26,034	$27,336	$101,779
NE	Creighton University	$38,406	$38,406	$38,406	$56,748	$171,966
NE	University of Nebraska Medical Center	$43,510	$45,686	$47,970	$50,368	$187,534
NH	Massachusetts College of Pharmacy and Health Sciences - Manchester	$51,600	$54,180	$56,889		$162,669
NJ	Fairleigh Dickinson University	$40,551	$42,579	$44,707	$46,943	$174,780
NJ	Rutgers, The State University of New Jersey	$38,199	$40,109	$42,114	$44,220	$164,642
NM	The University of New Mexico	$41,368	$43,436	$45,608	$47,889	$178,301

State	Pharmacy School	Year 1	Year 2	Year 3	Year 4	Total
NV	Roseman University of Health Sciences	$54,100	$56,805	$59,645		$170,550
NY	Albany College of Pharmacy and Health Sciences - Albany	$41,920	$44,016	$46,217	$48,528	$180,680
NY	D'Youville College	$35,034	$36,786	$38,625	$40,556	$151,001
NY	Stony Brook University	$27,000	$28,350	$29,768	$31,256	$116,373
NY	Touro College (NY)	$39,730	$39,730	$39,730	$39,730	$158,920
NY	Binghamton University	$40,899	$42,944	$45,091	$47,346	$176,280
NY	St. John Fisher College Wegmans	$40,674	$42,708	$44,843	$47,085	$175,310
NY	Long Island University	$42,258	$44,371	$46,589	$48,919	$182,137
NY	University at Buffalo	$50,122	$52,628	$55,260	$58,022	$216,032
OH	Northeast Ohio Medical University (NEOMED)	$36,097	$37,902	$39,797	$42,403	$156,199
OH	The Ohio State University	$43,360	$45,528	$47,804	$55,041	$191,733
OH	University of Cincinnati The James L. Winkle	$32,206	$32,206	$48,309	$32,206	$144,927
OH	Cedarville University	$35,682	$37,466	$39,339	$41,306	$153,794
OH	The University of Findlay	$42,030	$44,132	$46,338	$48,655	$181,155
OH	The University of Toledo	$26,701	$28,036	$41,371	$36,442	$132,550
OK	Southwestern Oklahoma State University	$38,435	$40,357	$42,375	$44,493	$165,660
OK	The University of Oklahoma	$43,552	$45,730	$48,016	$50,417	$187,715
OR	Pacific University Oregon	$46,667	$49,000	$51,450	$54,023	$201,141
OR	Oregon State University	$27,064	$28,417	$29,838	$31,330	$116,649
PA	Wilkes University Nesbitt	$36,982	$38,831	$40,773	$42,811	$159,397
PA	Lake Erie College of Osteopathic Medicine - Distance Education Pathway	$29,933	$31,430	$33,001	$34,651	$129,015

State	Pharmacy School	Year 1	Year 2	Year 3	Year 4	Total
PA	Lake Erie College of Osteopathic Medicine - Erie Campus	$32,141	$33,748	$35,435	$37,207	$138,532
PA	Temple University	$36,550	$38,378	$40,296	$42,311	$157,535
PA	Thomas Jefferson University	$39,043	$40,995	$43,045	$52,236	$175,319
PA	Duquesne University	$54,396	$57,116	$59,972	$62,970	$234,454
PA	University of Pittsburgh	$38,582	$40,511	$42,537	$44,663	$166,293
PA	University of the Sciences in Philadelphia	$30,000	$35,000	$35,000	$40,000	$140,000
PR	University of Puerto Rico	$8,500	$8,925	$9,371	$9,840	$36,636
SC	Medical University of South Carolina	$40,056	$42,059	$44,162	$45,369	$171,646
SC	Presbyterian College	$37,110	$38,966	$40,914	$42,959	$159,949
SC	University of South Carolina	$32,122	$33,728	$35,415	$34,185	$135,450
SC	South University (SC)	$36,972	$38,821	$40,762	$42,800	$159,354
TN	The University of Tennessee	$43,500	$45,675	$47,959	$50,357	$187,490
TN	Belmont University	$40,840	$42,882	$45,026	$47,277	$176,026
TN	Lipscomb University	$39,834	$41,826	$43,917	$46,113	$171,690
TN	South College (TN)	$47,900	$50,295	$52,810		$151,005
TN	Union University	$36,450	$38,273	$40,186	$42,195	$157,104
TN	East Tennessee State University	$38,827	$40,768	$42,807	$44,947	$167,349
TX	The University of Texas at El Paso	$34,000	$35,700	$37,485	$39,359	$146,544
TX	The University of Texas at Tyler Ben and Maytee Fisch	$34,686	$36,420	$38,241	$40,153	$149,501
TX	University of Houston	$32,258	$33,871	$35,564	$37,343	$139,036
TX	University of North Texas Health Science Center System	$36,664	$31,465	$38,126	$32,224	$138,479

State	Pharmacy School	Year 1	Year 2	Year 3	Year 4	Total
TX	University of the Incarnate Word Feik	$35,950	$37,748	$39,635	$41,617	$154,949
TX	Texas A&M University Irma Lerma Rangel	$18,880	$19,824	$20,815	$21,856	$81,375
TX	Texas Southern University	$31,920	$33,516	$35,192	$36,951	$137,579
TX	The University of Texas at Austin	$48,274	$50,688	$53,222	$55,883	$208,067
TX	Texas Tech University Health Sciences Center	$27,325	$28,691	$30,126	$31,632	$117,774
UT	University of Utah	$58,754	$61,692	$64,776	$68,015	$253,237
VA	Appalachian College of Pharmacy	$38,700	$40,635	$42,667		$122,002
VA	Shenandoah University	$36,410	$38,231	$40,142	$42,149	$156,932
VA	Virginia Commonwealth University	$23,828	$25,019	$26,270	$27,584	$102,702
VA	Hampton University	$31,474	$33,048	$34,700	$36,435	$135,657
VT	Albany College of Pharmacy and Health Sciences - Colchester	$41,920	$44,016	$46,217	$48,528	$180,680
WA	Washington State University	$39,226	$41,187	$43,247	$45,409	$169,069
WA	University of Washington	$52,263	$54,876	$57,620	$60,501	$225,260
WI	Medical College of Wisconsin Pharmacy School	$46,929	$49,275	$51,739		$147,944
WI	Concordia University Wisconsin	$36,771	$38,610	$40,540	$42,567	$158,488
WI	University of Wisconsin	$40,240	$42,252	$44,365	$50,512	$177,369
WV	Marshall University	$34,418	$34,418	$34,418	$23,852	$127,106
WV	University of Charleston	$32,088	$33,692	$35,377	$37,146	$138,303
WV	West Virginia University	$33,876	$35,570	$37,348	$39,216	$146,010
WY	University of Wyoming	$34,200	$35,910	$37,706	$39,591	$147,406

Table 2: PharmD Tuition from Least to Most Expensive

State	Pharmacy School	Year 1	Year 2	Year 3	Year 4	Total
PR	University of Puerto Rico	$8,500	$8,925	$9,371	$9,840	$36,636
TX	Texas A&M University	$18,880	$19,824	$20,815	$21,856	$81,375
MI	Ferris State University	$23,000	$24,150	$25,358	$26,625	$99,133
ND	North Dakota State University	$23,614	$24,795	$26,034	$27,336	$101,779
VA	Virginia Commonwealth University	$23,828	$25,019	$26,270	$27,584	$102,702
Lebanon	Lebanese American University	$25,620	$26,901	$28,246	$29,658	$110,425
NY	Stony Brook University	$27,000	$28,350	$29,768	$31,256	$116,373
OR	Oregon State University	$27,064	$28,417	$29,838	$31,330	$116,649
TX	Texas Tech University Health Sciences Center	$27,325	$28,691	$30,126	$31,632	$117,774
DC	Howard University	$28,000	$29,400	$30,870	$32,414	$120,684
VA	Appalachian College of Pharmacy	$38,700	$40,635	$42,667		$122,002
WV	Marshall University	$34,418	$34,418	$34,418	$23,852	$127,106
PA	Lake Erie College of Osteopathic Medicine - Distance Education Pathway	$29,933	$31,430	$33,001	$34,651	$129,015
MT	University of Montana Skaggs	$30,190	$31,700	$33,284	$34,949	$130,123
OH	The University of Toledo	$26,701	$28,036	$41,371	$36,442	$132,550
SC	University of South Carolina	$32,122	$33,728	$35,415	$34,185	$135,450
VA	Hampton University	$31,474	$33,048	$34,700	$36,435	$135,657
IL	Southern Illinois University	$31,894	$33,489	$35,163	$36,921	$137,467
TX	Texas Southern University	$31,920	$33,516	$35,192	$36,951	$137,579
FL	Larkin University	$45,492	$45,492	$46,715		$137,699

State	Pharmacy School	Year 1	Year 2	Year 3	Year 4	Total
WV	University of Charleston	$32,088	$33,692	$35,377	$37,146	$138,303
FL	Lake Erie College of Osteopathic Medicine - Bradenton Campus	$32,113	$33,719	$35,405	$37,175	$138,411
TX	University of North Texas Health Science Center	$36,664	$31,465	$38,126	$32,224	$138,479
PA	Lake Erie College of Osteopathic Medicine - Erie Campus	$32,141	$33,748	$35,435	$37,207	$138,532
TX	University of Houston	$32,258	$33,871	$35,564	$37,343	$139,036
FL	Palm Beach Atlantic University	$37,800	$37,800	$37,800	$25,864	$139,264
GA	Mercer University	$30,000	$35,000	$35,000	$40,000	$140,000
PA	University of the Sciences in Philadelphia	$30,000	$35,000	$35,000	$40,000	$140,000
NC	Wingate University -Hendersonville	$33,244	$34,906	$36,652	$38,484	$143,286
NC	Wingate University - Wingate	$33,244	$34,906	$36,652	$38,484	$143,286
OH	University of Cincinnati	$32,206	$32,206	$48,309	$32,206	$144,927
LA	Xavier University of Louisiana	$33,640	$35,322	$37,088	$38,943	$144,993
ME	Husson University	$37,074	$35,070	$42,084	$31,062	$145,290
WV	West Virginia University	$33,876	$35,570	$37,348	$39,216	$146,010
TX	The University of Texas at El Paso	$34,000	$35,700	$37,485	$39,359	$146,544
WY	University of Wyoming	$34,200	$35,910	$37,706	$39,591	$147,406
WI	Medical College of Wisconsin Pharmacy School	$46,929	$49,275	$51,739		$147,944
TX	The University of Texas at Tyler Ben and Maytee Fisch	$34,686	$36,420	$38,241	$40,153	$149,501
NY	D'Youville College School of Pharmacy	$35,034	$36,786	$38,625	$40,556	$151,001
TN	South College	$47,900	$50,295	$52,810		$151,005

State	Pharmacy School	Year 1	Year 2	Year 3	Year 4	Total
GA	University of Georgia	$36,850	$41,458	$36,850	$36,850	$152,008
MA	Massachusetts College of Pharmacy and Health Sciences - Boston	$32,600	$38,300	$40,215	$42,226	$153,341
OH	Cedarville University School of Pharmacy	$35,682	$37,466	$39,339	$41,306	$153,794
TX	University of the Incarnate Word	$35,950	$37,748	$39,635	$41,617	$154,949
FL	University of Florida	$36,000	$37,800	$39,690	$41,675	$155,165
FL	University of South Florida	$36,000	$37,800	$39,690	$41,675	$155,165
OH	Northeast Ohio Medical University (NEOMED)	$36,097	$37,902	$39,797	$42,403	$156,199
NC	Campbell University	$39,200	$39,200	$39,200	$39,200	$156,800
VA	Shenandoah University	$36,410	$38,231	$40,142	$42,149	$156,932
TN	Union University	$36,450	$38,273	$40,186	$42,195	$157,104
CO	Regis University	$36,460	$38,283	$40,197	$42,207	$157,147
IL	Rosalind Franklin University of Medicine and Science	$36,463	$38,286	$40,200	$42,210	$157,160
PA	Temple University	$36,550	$38,378	$40,296	$42,311	$157,535
FL	Florida A&M University	$36,566	$38,394	$40,314	$42,330	$157,604
WI	Concordia University Wisconsin	$36,771	$38,610	$40,540	$42,567	$158,488
NY	Touro College (NY)	$39,730	$39,730	$39,730	$39,730	$158,920
GA	South University (GA)	$36,972	$38,821	$40,762	$42,800	$159,354
SC	South University (SC)	$36,972	$38,821	$40,762	$42,800	$159,354
PA	Wilkes University Nesbitt	$36,982	$38,831	$40,773	$42,811	$159,397
SC	Presbyterian College	$37,110	$38,966	$40,914	$42,959	$159,949

State	Pharmacy School	Year 1	Year 2	Year 3	Year 4	Total
MA	Massachusetts College of Pharmacy and Health Sciences - Worcester	$51,600	$54,180	$56,889		$162,669
NH	Massachusetts College of Pharmacy and Health Sciences - Manchester	$51,600	$54,180	$56,889		$162,669
NJ	Rutgers, The State University of New Jersey	$38,199	$40,109	$42,114	$44,220	$164,642
MI	University of Michigan	$36,666	$36,666	$36,666	$54,999	$164,997
ID	Idaho State University	$38,312	$40,228	$42,239	$44,351	$165,130
CA	University of California, San Diego	$40,427	$40,327	$44,432	$40,327	$165,513
FL	Nova Southeastern University	$38,425	$40,346	$42,364	$44,482	$165,617
OK	Southwestern Oklahoma State University	$38,435	$40,357	$42,375	$44,493	$165,660
GA	Philadelphia College of Osteopathic Medicine - Georgia Campus	$41,538	$41,538	$41,538	$41,538	$166,152
PA	University of Pittsburgh	$38,582	$40,511	$42,537	$44,663	$166,293
HI	University of Hawaii at Hilo	$41,248	$41,498	$41,738	$41,978	$166,462
MD	Notre Dame of Maryland University	$38,750	$40,688	$42,722	$44,858	$167,017
TN	East Tennessee State University Bill Gatton	$38,827	$40,768	$42,807	$44,947	$167,349
IA	Drake University	$40,572	$40,572	$40,572	$45,662	$167,378
AR	Harding University	$39,030	$40,982	$43,031	$45,182	$168,224
WA	Washington State University	$39,226	$41,187	$43,247	$45,409	$169,069
IL	Chicago State University	$39,410	$41,381	$43,450	$45,622	$169,862
NV	Roseman University of Health Sciences	$54,100	$56,805	$59,645		$170,550
IN	Manchester University	$39,780	$41,769	$43,857	$46,050	$171,457
SC	Medical University of South Carolina	$40,056	$42,059	$44,162	$45,369	$171,646
TN	Lipscomb University	$39,834	$41,826	$43,917	$46,113	$171,690

State	Pharmacy School	Year 1	Year 2	Year 3	Year 4	Total
CO	University of Colorado	$39,870	$41,864	$43,957	$46,155	$171,845
NE	Creighton University	$38,406	$38,406	$38,406	$56,748	$171,966
MS	William Carey University	$40,000	$42,000	$44,100	$46,305	$172,405
MN	University of Minnesota	$41,666	$41,666	$43,749	$45,937	$173,018
IN	Purdue University	$40,276	$42,290	$44,404	$46,625	$173,595
NC	High Point University	$40,522	$42,548	$44,676	$46,909	$174,655
NJ	Fairleigh Dickinson University	$40,551	$42,579	$44,707	$46,943	$174,780
IN	Butler University	$42,790	$42,790	$42,790	$46,590	$174,960
NY	St. John Fisher College	$40,674	$42,708	$44,843	$47,085	$175,310
PA	Thomas Jefferson University	$39,043	$40,995	$43,045	$52,236	$175,319
TN	Belmont University	$40,840	$42,882	$45,026	$47,277	$176,026
NY	Binghamton University - SUNY	$40,899	$42,944	$45,091	$47,346	$176,280
AL	Auburn University Harrison	$41,108	$43,163	$45,322	$47,588	$177,181
WI	University of Wisconsin	$40,240	$42,252	$44,365	$50,512	$177,369
NM	The University of New Mexico	$41,368	$43,436	$45,608	$47,889	$178,301
KY	Sullivan University	$56,620	$59,451	$62,424		$178,495
KS	The University of Kansas	$41,480	$43,554	$45,732	$48,018	$178,784
NY	Albany College of Pharmacy and Health Sciences - Albany	$41,920	$44,016	$46,217	$48,528	$180,680
VT	Albany College of Pharmacy and Health Sciences - Colchester	$41,920	$44,016	$46,217	$48,528	$180,680
OH	The University of Findlay	$42,030	$44,132	$46,338	$48,655	$181,155
NY	Long Island University	$42,258	$44,371	$46,589	$48,919	$182,137

State	Pharmacy School	Year 1	Year 2	Year 3	Year 4	Total
ME	University of New England	$42,805	$44,945	$47,193	$49,552	$184,495
AR	University of Arkansas for Medical Sciences	$42,806	$44,946	$47,194	$49,553	$184,499
CT	University of Connecticut	$36,948	$38,795	$53,552	$56,230	$185,525
CA	Chapman University	$69,750	$69,750	$46,500		$186,000
TN	The University of Tennessee	$43,500	$45,675	$47,959	$50,357	$187,490
NE	University of Nebraska Medical Center	$43,510	$45,686	$47,970	$50,368	$187,534
OK	The University of Oklahoma	$43,552	$45,730	$48,016	$50,417	$187,715
MA	Western New England University	$43,596	$45,776	$48,065	$50,468	$187,904
LA	The University of Louisiana Monroe	$43,718	$45,904	$48,199	$50,609	$188,430
CA	West Coast University	$43,780	$45,969	$48,267	$50,681	$188,697
CA	University of California, San Francisco	$63,809	$63,809	$63,809		$191,427
OH	The Ohio State University	$43,360	$45,528	$47,804	$55,041	$191,733
IA	The University of Iowa	$44,790	$47,030	$49,381	$51,850	$193,051
IL	University of Illinois at Chicago	$44,799	$47,039	$49,391	$51,860	$193,089
MD	University of Maryland	$44,900	$47,145	$49,502	$51,977	$193,525
NC	The University of North Carolina (UNC) at Chapel Hill	$51,894	$45,356	$51,894	$45,356	$194,500
CA	California Health Sciences University	$45,605	$47,885	$50,280	$52,793	$196,563
MI	Wayne State University	$51,063	$55,764	$46,056	$44,489	$197,372
CA	California Northstate University	$49,520	$49,310	$49,638	$48,910	$197,378
AZ	Midwestern University - Glendale Campus	$45,909	$48,204	$50,615	$53,145	$197,874
IL	Midwestern University - Downers Grove Campus	$45,909	$48,204	$50,615	$53,145	$197,874

State	Pharmacy School	Year 1	Year 2	Year 3	Year 4	Total
CA	Western University of Health Sciences	$49,725	$49,725	$49,725	$50,075	$199,250
OR	Pacific University Oregon	$46,667	$49,000	$51,450	$54,023	$201,141
MS	The University of Mississippi	$48,534	$48,534	$52,072	$52,072	$201,212
CA	Keck Graduate Institute	$46,900	$49,245	$51,707	$54,293	$202,145
AZ	University of Arizona	$47,060	$49,413	$51,884	$54,478	$202,834
CA	Touro University California	$47,200	$49,560	$52,038	$54,640	$203,438
CA	Loma Linda University	$47,364	$49,732	$52,219	$54,830	$204,145
MA	Northeastern University	$47,720	$50,106	$52,611	$55,242	$205,679
AL	Samford University McWhorter	$47,826	$50,217	$52,728	$55,365	$206,136
TX	The University of Texas at Austin	$48,274	$50,688	$53,222	$55,883	$208,067
CA	University of the Pacific	$79,148	$79,148	$52,772		$211,068
CA	Marshall B. Ketchum University	$49,430	$51,902	$54,497	$57,221	$213,049
NY	University at Buffalo - SUNY	$50,122	$52,628	$55,260	$58,022	$216,032
CT	University of Saint Joseph	$50,569	$53,097	$55,752	$58,540	$217,959
KY	University of Kentucky	$50,665	$53,198	$55,858	$58,651	$218,372
IL	Roosevelt University	$50,902	$53,447	$56,119	$58,925	$219,394
MO	University of Missouri-Kansas City	$51,476	$54,050	$56,752	$59,590	$221,868
WA	University of Washington	$52,263	$54,876	$57,620	$60,501	$225,260
CA	University of Southern California	$56,846	$56,846	$56,846	$56,846	$227,384
PA	Duquesne University	$54,396	$57,116	$59,972	$62,970	$234,454
UT	University of Utah	$58,754	$61,692	$64,776	$68,015	$253,237
MD	University of Maryland Eastern Shore	$60,135	$63,142	$66,299	$69,614	$259,189

Calculating the actual cost of a PharmD degree

Before we dive into the numbers, keep in mind that students attending graduate school or professional school can take out federal student loans from the Direct Loans program. Direct Unsubsidized Loans, also known as Unsubsidized Stafford Loans, offer a fixed interest rate and flexible repayment terms. Financial need is not required to qualify. Students are responsible for paying all the interest that adds up until the loan balance is paid off.

Interest Rates and Fees

The interest rates on Direct Unsubsidized Loans for professional students are fixed and do not change over the life of the loan. The interest rate for Direct Unsubsidized Loans for the 2018–2019 academic year is 6.6%. This is lower than the 7.6% interest rate on Grad PLUS Loans. As students can only borrow up to $20,500 per year for the Direct Unsubsidized Loan, they will have to take the higher interest Grad PLUS Loan to help pay for the remaining cost of their pharmacy education.

The interest on a Direct Unsubsidized Loan starts to accrue (add up) from the date the loan is first disbursed. If you don't pay the interest as it accrues, it will be capitalized (added to the loan balance), increasing the size of the loan.

Fees on Direct Unsubsidized Loans

The current fee (loans first disbursed on Oct. 1, 2017 and before Oct. 1, 2018) on the Direct Unsubsidized Loan for graduate students is 1.062%. This is less expensive than the 4.248% fee on Grad PLUS Loans.

How Fees Affect the Total Loan Cost

Loan fees are basically a form of up-front interest. For example, if your loan has a 10-year repayment term, a 4% fee is the same as an increase of about 0.875% to 1% in the interest rate. If your loan has a 30-year repayment term, a 4% fee is the same as an increase of about 0.334% to 0.5% in the interest rate.

Direct Unsubsidized Loan

- 6.6% fixed interest rate
- 1.062% fee
- Demonstrated financial need not required
- Annual borrowing limit: $20,500
- You are responsible for paying all interest

Grad PLUS Loan

- 7.6% fixed interest rate
- 4.248% fee
- Demonstrated financial need not required
- Annual borrowing limit: Cost of Attendance (COA) minus other financial aid received
- You are responsible for paying all interest

In-School Deferment and Grace Period[2]

While you are enrolled in school at least half time, your Direct Loan will be placed into deferment, which means you do not have to make any payments. In addition, you do not have to make payments during the six-month grace period after you graduate or drop below half-time enrollment status. The interest on your loan will start to accrue as soon as loan funds are sent to your school. Even though you aren't making any payments, interest is still adding up.

The actual costs vary depending on the following factors: the school you attend, the length of the PharmD program, cost of living, total loan amount borrowed and interest rate.

In the event you choose to take out student loans, the interest rate for a Direct Unsubsidized Stafford Loan (for graduate or professional students) is 6.6%, as of July 2018. The example given below is of a pharmacy student attending ABC University College of Pharmacy.

Let's call this student Jackie. We will assume Jackie has *no* money and will be borrowing the maximum amount of loan disbursed in two installments (the first one in the fall semester and the second one in the spring semester) with $35,000 in each phase. We will also assume Jackie is focused only on studying, does not work part time, and therefore will not contribute any money into paying her loan while she is in school.

From the start of the first disbursed amount to the start of the second disbursed amount = five months. And from the start of the second disbursed amount to the start of the second year = seven months. Remember, interest starts accruing the moment the funds are disbursed.[1]

Table 3: Sample Total Expenses of Four-Year Pharmacy School

	First Year	Second Year	Third Year	Fourth year	Total
Tuition and Fees	$50,000	$50,000	$50,000	$50,000	$200,000
Living Expenses	$20,000	$20,000	$20,000	$20,000	$80,000
Total Interest Accrued	$4,050	$9,624	$15,606	$22,026	$51,306
Loan Origination Fees	$2,320	$2,320	$2,320	$2,320	$9,280

The total amount you owe (1st year - 4th year) the day you graduate = $340,586

If you are curious about how everything is calculated, see below:

First Year:

Tuition and Fees: $50,000

Living Expenses: $20,000

Your annual living expenses of $20,000 is equal to $1667 per month.

Table 4: Monthly Living Expenses

Living Expenses Per Month		
Food	$7 per meal, 3x per day for 30 days	$630
Rent	A private room in a two-bedroom apartment in California	$800
Transportation	Gas and maintenance, assuming no car payments	$137
Miscellaneous	Entertainment, movies, Netflix	$100

Total Loan Amount Taken: Tuition and Fees + Living expenses = $70,000 (to be disbursed in 2 installments with $35,000 in each) Each $35,000 is made up of $10,250 Direct Unsubsidized Loan and $24,750 Grad PLUS Loan

Total Interest accrued by the end of first year:

= One year of interest on the 1st disbursed amount + 7 months of interest on the 2nd disbursed amount

= $10,250 x 6.6% + $24,750 x 7.6% + ($10,250 x 6.6%)/12 x 7 + ($24,750 x 7.6%)/12 x 7

= 677 + 1,881 + 395 + 1,097

= **$4,050**

Total amount owed by the end of first year:

= Total Loan Amount Taken + Interest + origination fees

= $70,000 + $4,050 + $217 + $2,103 = **$76,370**

Second Year:

Tuition and Fees: $50,000

Living Expenses: $20,000

Total Loan Amount Taken: $70,000 (to be disbursed in 2 installments of $35,000 each). Each $35,000 is made up of $10,250 Direct Unsubsidized Loan and $24,750 Grad PLUS Loan

Note that about 30% (29.3% to be exact) of the loan comes from Direct Unsubsidized Loan and 70% of the loan comes from Grad PLUS Loan. We will use this information to calculate the interest accrued from the first year total amount owed ($76,370).

Total Interest accrued by the end of second year:

= ($76,370 x 30%) x 6.6% + ($76,370 x 70%) x 7.6% + $10,250 x 6.6% + $24,750 x 7.6% + ($10,250 x 6.6%)/12 x 7 + ($24,750 x 7.6%)/12 x 7

= 1,512 + 4,062 + 677 + 1,881 + 395 + 1,097

= **$9,624**

Total amount owed by the end of second year:

= Total Loan Amount Owed from First Year + Total Loan Amount Owed from second year + Total Interest accrued by the end of second year + origination fees

= $76,370 + $70,000 + $9,624 + $217 + $2,103= **$158,314**

Third Year:

Tuition and Fees: $50,000

Living Expenses: $20,000

Total Loan Amount Taken: $70,000 (to be disbursed in 2 installments of $35,000 each). Each $35,000 is made up of $10,250 Direct Unsubsidized Loan and $24,750 Grad PLUS Loan

Total Interest accrued by the end of third year:

= ($158,314 x 30%) x 6.6% + ($158,314 x 70%) x 7.6% + $10,250 x 6.6% + $24,750 x 7.6% + ($10,250 x 6.6%)/12 x 7 + ($24,750 x 7.6%)/12 x 7

= 3,134 + 8,422 + 677 + 1,881 + 395 + 1,097

= **$15,606**

Total amount owed by the end of third year:

= Total Loan Amount Owed from First and Second Year + Total Loan Amount from third year + Interest accrued by the end of third year + origination fees

= $158,314 + $70,000 + $15,606 + $217 + $2,103 = **$246,240**

Fourth Year:

Tuition and Fees: $50,000

Living Expenses: $20,000

Total Loan Amount Taken: $70,000 (to be disbursed in 2 installments of $35,000 each). Each $35,000 is made up of $10,250 Direct Unsubsidized Loan and $24,750 Grad PLUS Loan

Total Interest accrued by the end of fourth year:

= ($246,240 x 30%) x 6.6% + ($246,240 x 70%) x 7.6% + $10,250 x 6.6% + $24,750 x 7.6% + ($10,250 x 6.6%)/12 x 7 + ($24,750 x 7.6%)/12 x 7

= 4,876 + 13,100 + 677 + 1,881 + 395 + 1,097

= **$22,026**

Total amount owed by the end of fourth year:

= Total Loan Amount Owed from First, Second, and Third Year + Total Loan Amount from 4th year + Total Interest accrued by the end of third year + origination fees

= 246,240 + 70,000 + 22,026 + $217 + $2,103 = **$340,586**

With this loan amount, what is the payment you need to make per month? Take a look at the examples given in the table below.

If the interest rate is 6.6%, the monthly payment will be as follow

Loan Amount	Interest Rate	10 Year Plan	15 Year Plan	20 Year Plan
$360,000	6.6%	$4,106	$3,155	$2,705
$280,000	6.6%	$3,194	$2,454	$2,104
$200,000	6.6%	$2,281	$1,753	$1,503

If the interest rate is 7.1%, the monthly payment amount will be slightly higher

Loan Amount	Interest Rate	10 Year Plan	15 Year Plan	20 Year Plan
$360,000	7.1%	$4,198	$3,255	$2,813
$280,000	7.1%	$3,265	$2,532	$2,188
$200,000	7.1%	$2,332	$1,808	$1,563

Tuition and fees alone for four years of pharmacy school education equal $200,000. After we take into consideration the estimated living expenses and all the interests that accrue, the total cost comes out to be $340,586. That's a lot of money.

Before you start cracking open childhood piggy banks, fear not; there are methods to decrease this financial madness and ensure that you are not entrenched in debt by the time you graduate from pharmacy school. With planning and preparation, you can minimize your student loans thereby shortening the time it takes for you to pay those loans off. Goodbye loans and hello shiny keys to your Corvette and contemporary condo.

Ways to Ward off High Student Loans:

1. **Attend a lower tuition pharmacy school.** This option has its pros and cons. If you are in a low-tuition state, take advantage of that. If you are in a state like California where pharmacy school tuition is sky-high, consider attending an out-of-state pharmacy school to lower your costs. You can always return home after graduation—for example, many of our colleagues have returned to California after their graduate studies to accept new jobs! Or you might fall in love with your state of choice and end up working there. Tuition fees play a major role in determining your total graduate degree costs, so don't be afraid to explore other options in order to keep your student loan payments at a more manageable level.
2. **Work throughout pharmacy school.** Find a part-time pharmacy internship and use the money you earn to make payments towards your accrued interest. As shown in the tables above, interest accrues quickly, so being able to put money towards it while you're still in school puts you in an advantageous position. If you are able to find work as a pharmacy intern while attending pharmacy school, seize the opportunity to do some networking at the same time and make some of those crucial professional connections.
3. **Live with housemates close to school.** Live like a college student if you want to avoid getting buried in graduate student debt. You can save a big chunk of your living expenses by living with housemates in a location close to school. Split your living costs and cut down your transportation expenses at the same time.
4. **Live like a student AFTER you graduate (for a few years).** Your social media will be flooded with your classmates' purchases soon after graduation. A new house, new apartment, a multi-country

cruise... Don't be like them. Be smart and live below your means; pay off your debt for a few years until you have a handle on your finances.

5. **Cook at home rather than eat out.** When you're in pharmacy school, sparing 30 minutes to an hour to cook at home can seem daunting amongst all the studying. With tasty takeout options just a couple of smartphone swipes away, the temptation is always there. In the long run, cooking at home is cheaper and healthier. A takeout meal averages about $10 [3], but you can cook something similar at home for $4.

   And home cooking doesn't have to mean selling your soul to the instant ramen gods. There is a plethora of websites, video channels, and blogs that will teach you to up your cooking game while keeping your budget on the straight and narrow. If your hunger just can't wait, we've included some of our favorites below:

   - 7 Pharmacy School-Friendly Microwave Meals (https://bit.ly/2gfjnrh)
   - 6 Low-Cost Meal Preps (https://bit.ly/2QYRljN)
   - 4 Meals Anyone Can Make (https://bit.ly/2FGd1ZA)

6

ACCELERATED PHARMACY PROGRAMS

"I have so much that I want to do. I hate wasting time."
– Stephen Hawking

IF YOU'RE A HIGH schooler (or are researching on behalf of someone in high school who is interested in a career in pharmacy), this is for you. We won't be going into great detail in this chapter but want to at least get you started.

If you know pharmacy is your calling, you may want to consider these accelerated programs below that combine undergraduate programs with a PharmD degree. These accelerated programs are typically six to seven years long with the exception of a five-year program at University of the Pacific. If an 18-year-old graduates from high school and is accepted into an accelerated program they will be a full-fledged pharmacist at 24 years old! We've met several pharmacists who took this route and, by the time we were chatting, they had hit major milestones in their pharmacy careers before they even hit their 30s.

Table 1: Accelerated Pharmacy Programs for High School Students

Location	School	Length of the Program
Albany, NY	Albany College of Pharmacy and Health Sciences [1]	6 years
Boston, MA	Massachusetts College of Pharmacy and Health Sciences [2]	5 - 6 years
Ada, OH	Ohio Northern University College of Pharmacy [3]	6 years
Findlay, OH	The University of Findlay [4]	6 years
New Jersey, NJ	Rutgers University, Ernest Mario School of Pharmacy [5]	6 years
Brookings, SD	South Dakota State University College of Pharmacy and Allied Health Professions [6]	6 years
Queens, NY	St. John's University College of Pharmacy and Health Sciences [7]	6 years
Missouri, MO	St. Louis College of Pharmacy [8]	7 years
Kingston, RI	The University of Rhode Island College of Pharmacy [9]	6 years
Stockton, CA	University of the Pacific [10]	5 - 7 years
Philadelphia, PA	University of the Sciences in Philadelphia [11]	6 years

If you have a bachelor, master, or more advanced degree, there are schools that allow you to obtain a PharmD in 3 years. These schools are compiled in the table below.

Table 2: Three-Year PharmD Programs (Bachelor Degree Required)

State	School
Stockton, CA	University of the Pacific Thomas J. Long School of Pharmacy and Health Sciences
San Francisco, CA	University of California, San Francisco School of Pharmacy
Irvine, CA	Chapman University School of Pharmacy
Miami, FL	Larkin University College of Pharmacy
Louisville, KY	Sullivan University College of Pharmacy
Worcester, MA	Massachusetts College of Pharmacy and Health Sciences - Worcester
Manchester, NH	Massachusetts College of Pharmacy and Health Sciences - Manchester
Henderson, NV	Roseman University of Health Sciences
Knoxville, TN	South College (TN) School of Pharmacy
Oakwood, VA	Appalachian College of Pharmacy
Milwaukee, WI	Medical College of Wisconsin Pharmacy School

7

THE SMART APPLICATION GAME PLAN

"You miss 100% of the shots you don't take." – Wayne Gretzky

Application Timeline and Checklist

This timeline is based on a typical four-year college degree and provides a pretty generous timeline, especially if you are an advanced planner.

1st and 2nd year of college	☐ Get involved with your school's Pre-Pharmacy Club ☐ Look for part-time job, research, and volunteer opportunities related to pharmacy ☐ Keep a journal of inspirational experiences (this will help with your personal statement and interview) ☐ Take pharmacy prerequisite courses ☐ Network and develop excellent relationships with faculty/ teaching assistants (TAs)/pharmacists ☐ Research and attend open houses (or information sessions) for pharmacy schools you are interested in
3rd year of college	☐ Pick which pharmacy schools you are applying to ○ Make sure you are completing their required prerequisite courses ○ Record all their dates and deadlines ☐ January — Take your Pharmacy College Admissions Test (PCAT) (optional) ☐ Start writing your personal statements (give yourself at least six months to write a strong one)

	☐ March – July o Ask faculty/pharmacists for a letter of recommendation. Give them all necessary information *at least* three months in advance. o Create a file for each writer and include: resume/CV, personal statement, transcripts, and PharmCAS submission instructions
4th year of college	☐ Mid-July — PharmCAS application available ☐ September — early decision deadline ☐ Late October — early November: Submit your completed PharmCAS application ☐ Submit your supplemental application per school instructions ☐ September to March: Prepare for interviews and practice lots of mock interviews. **Eat, sleep, and breathe interview practice!**

Pharmacy College Application Service (PharmCAS)

The Pharmacy College Application Service at www.pharmcas.org is the centralized service that allows applicants to use a single application to apply to multiple PharmD degree programs.

When should I apply to PharmCAS?

As soon as possible! Start the application early to ensure you have ample time to fulfill all the requirements specified by the schools you plan on applying to. The PharmCAS application cycle begins in mid-July for the fall enrollment of the following year. We recommend you start your PharmCAS application as soon as it is available. Pharmacy schools start reviewing applications as they are submitted. With a limited amount of interview slots available, it is imperative that you submit your application as early as you can as that will give you a higher chance of getting interviewed.

Through PharmCAS, you will be able to apply to most of the pharmacy schools in the United States. Bookmark the PharmCAS website on your browser since you'll refer to it often.

Additional PharmCAS services:

- Pharmacy school search with the following four filters:
  - Search by location
    - **West:** Idaho, Montana, Wyoming, Nevada, Utah, Colorado, Arizona, New Mexico, Alaska, Washington, Oregon, California, Hawaii
    - **Midwest:** Wisconsin, Michigan, Illinois, Indiana, Ohio, Missouri, North Dakota, South Dakota, Nebraska, Kansas, Minnesota, Iowa

        - **South:** Delaware, Maryland, District of Columbia, Virginia, West Virginia, North Carolina, South Carolina, Georgia, Florida, Kentucky, Tennessee, Mississippi, Alabama, Oklahoma, Texas, Arkansas, Louisiana
        - **Northeast:** Maine, New Hampshire, Vermont, Massachusetts, Rhode Island, Connecticut, New York, Pennsylvania, New Jersey
    - Search by test requirements
        - PCAT exam
        - TOEFL (Test of English as a First Language) exam
    - Search by school status
        - Public
        - Private
    - Search by residency requirements
        - Foreign Citizens Consideration
        - US Residency Requirement
        - Proof of State Residency Requirement
- Detailed information on each pharmacy program including:
    - Contact Information
    - Program Deadline
    - Accreditation Status
    - Program Information
    - Program Description
    - Program Statistics and Criteria
    - Program Prerequisites
    - Supplemental Application
    - Test Requirements: PCAT, TOEFL

- Experience Requirement
- Residency Requirement
- Letter of Reference
- Interviews
- Accepted Applicants profile

Early Decision

If you have a dream school that you would immediately jump at the chance to attend if admitted, you can opt for early decision. However, it's important to note that you can only apply for early decision to **one** school and it is a binding contract if you get accepted.[1] If you are applying for early decision, make sure you contact the school of your choice and that you meet all their prerequisite requirements. Ensure that your transcripts, application, essays, and letters of recommendation are submitted by the early decision deadline (they tend to be in September). Typically, you'll find out what their decision is by mid-October. If you are offered admission under early decision, it is expected that you will accept the offer. If you are denied early decision admission, shrug it off. You can still apply through the regular admissions process!

How many schools should I apply to?

It depends on your situation. Take a look at the application fee payment table below. Applying to pharmacy schools is **not** free, so if your strategy is to apply to *all* the schools in the United States and pray that one accepts you, think again.

Not unlike the undergraduate school selection process, pick one to two schools in each of the following categories to apply to:

- Safety schools - schools you know you have a really good chance (95%) of getting into based on your application.
- Target schools - schools you know you have a decent chance (50%) of getting into based on your application.
- Reach schools - schools you know you have a low chance (25%) of getting into based on your application.

We cover the grades aspect of this in the *GPA* section in Chapter 8 if you'd like to learn more about how your GPA impacts your pharmacy school application.

Application Fees Payment Per Schools for 2018-2019 [2]

Number of PharmCAS Degree Program Designations	PharmCAS Fee Due
1	$175
2	$230
3	$285
4	$340
5	$395
6	$450
7	$505
8	$560
9	$615
10	$670
11 or more	Add $55.00 for each additional degree program

8

BECOME UNREJECTABLE AND GET ACCEPTED ANYWHERE

"Opportunities don't happen, you create them."
– Chris Grosser

WHAT ARE ALL THE major components of my pharmacy applicant portfolio and how do I maximize each one?

Major

What major should I choose for undergraduate studies?

It's a misconception that you need a science major in undergraduate studies to be competitive. Students who declare themselves as pre-med or pre-pharmacy traditionally major in biology, chemistry, biochemistry, neuroscience, chemical engineering, pharmaceutical science, physics, psychobiology, etc. It looks great on paper when students obtain a high GPA with tough science majors, but if your goal is to simply attend pharmacy school and you're not a super genius science wiz, it's better to ace your prerequisite pharmacy science courses and study a major you enjoy.

How do pharmacy schools calculate GPA?

Pharmacy schools typically calculate two types of GPAs—your GPA for the pharmacy prerequisite courses (i.e. general chemistry, organic chemistry, calculus, etc.) and your overall GPA. It is vital to do extremely well in your pharmacy prerequisite courses. Typically, pharmacy schools weight applicants' prerequisite GPAs more heavily than their overall GPA. They look at your overall profile as an applicant: your GPA, motivation to become a pharmacist through personal statements, your work experience, extracurricular activities, letters of recommendation, PCAT scores (for schools that require it), and your communication skills. Schools will evaluate these criteria to see your potential to excel in your pharmacy courses, pass your board examination, and succeed as a pharmacist. In a nutshell, schools are looking for self-motivated individuals who care for the well-being of others and will do what it takes to achieve their goals.

Grade Point Average (GPA)

Super Star Applicant: GPA 3.6+

Amazing. You are definitely a very competitive applicant! Having a high GPA will definitely open doors to all the pharmacy schools because that is the first thing a school will look at before attending to other aspects of your application portfolio. Even with a high GPA, you will need a solid essay, sparkling letters of recommendation, strong interview skills, and no red flags on your completed application.

Even if your profile is outstanding, your grades are amazing, and you're the type of applicant that admission departments dream of interviewing, you should still apply to at least two backup "safety" schools. The worst thing you could do to yourself is to get overconfident and apply to just ONE amazing school, be rejected from that amazing school, and have to start the process all over the following year. Don't obsess over an acceptance from your dream school to the point that it becomes a bottleneck to your pharmacy career goals.

Typical Applicant: GPA 3.2–3.5

This is where the majority of pharmacy school applicants will start their application journey. While you may not be an outstanding applicant with a GPA in this range, your admission chances are actually very solid. You can make yourself stand out with a superb essay, extensive pharmacy-related experiences, amazing letters of recommendation, and mind-blowing interview skills.

When applying, you may want to apply to more than one school in each of the following categories: safety, target and reach schools. Our recommendation of pharmacy schools would be at least two in each category, which translates to at least six schools total you should be applying to. If you are conservative, applying to three schools in each category would be most ideal in increasing your chances of getting accepted.

Challenged Applicant: GPA 2.8-3.1

Contrary to common belief, students with a GPA of less than 3.0 **do** have a chance of getting into a pharmacy school, so don't abandon all hope. If you are in this category, you must first believe that you do have a shot! Strategy is key. Students in this category should apply to schools that accept students at a lower GPA range and consider schools that are newly opened or not yet accredited. Refer to Table 3 ***Pharmacy Schools Sorted by Average GPA of Admitted Students in 2018 Entering Class*** to find out the average GPA of students admitted to a school from lowest GPA average to highest GPA average. Although these schools are not favorably looked upon as compared to the more established ones, they do prepare you for the pharmacy board examinations that license you as a pharmacist (just like any other pharmacy school).

If pharmacy is your passion and you dream of one day becoming a pharmacist, come up with a plan, focus on the areas in which you can improve, and highlight your strengths. You can make up for your lower GPA by having a very strong personal statement, meaningful pharmacy-related experiences, stunning letters of recommendation, and mastering your interview skills. When applying, you may want to apply to at least three schools in each of the following categories: safety, target and reach schools.

Should I bother to apply if my GPA is less than 2.5?

We'll be honest here: if your GPA falls under 2.5, your chance of getting into pharmacy school is going to be a longshot. Although you might need somewhat of a miracle to get into a pharmacy school, having the following will tremendously help improve your chances: upward GPA trend, incredible PCAT score, extensive pharmacy experience, having had a big impact in the local community or a graduate degree with a better GPA performance. It will be exceedingly tough, but if you are truly passionate about pursuing a pharmacy degree and can make up for a weak GPA in the areas listed above, you could just end up with the admission you desire.

However, if your GPA is less than 2.5 and you want to go to pharmacy school, you really need to ask yourself how badly you want to be a pharmacist and what you are willing to put into that goal. Until those two questions are answered, you should not be applying to any pharmacy school. If you are not committed to doing what it takes to succeed and are not able to show that level of seriousness to the admission officer, your chance of being admitted is literally close to zero. True, not every pharmacist began their pharmacy studies as a standout applicant, but meeting or barely meeting the minimum GPA requirement means that you really need to take a hard look at whether you have the drive and work ethic to succeed in pharmacy school.

How do I know which schools give me the best shot at admission based on my GPA?

Below are three tables that will help you identify the schools you want to apply to. The tables sort schools by state, minimum GPA required to apply, and the average admitted GPA (in ascending order). These tables will help you quickly determine which school you are eligible to apply to and give you an idea of your chance of being accepted (by comparing your GPA to the average admitted GPA). If you have a state of preference, you will find the one sorted by state very useful. If you want to see the Excel version of these tables, please check out the Resource section for the link to download the files.

State Abbreviation Reference

State	Abbreviation	State	Abbreviation
Alabama	AL	Montana	MT
Alaska	AK	Nebraska	NE
Arizona	AZ	Nevada	NV
Arkansas	AR	New Hampshire	NH
California	CA	New Jersey	NJ
Colorado	CO	New Mexico	NM
Connecticut	CT	New York	NY
Delaware	DE	North Carolina	NC
Florida	FL	North Dakota	ND
Georgia	GA	Ohio	OH
Hawaii	HI	Oklahoma	OK
Idaho	ID	Oregon	OR
Illinois	IL	Pennsylvania	PA
Indiana	IN	Rhode Island	RI
Iowa	IA	South Carolina	SC
Kansas	KS	South Dakota	SD
Kentucky	KY	Tennessee	TN
Louisiana	LA	Texas	TX
Maine	ME	Utah	UT
Maryland	MD	Vermont	VT
Massachusetts	MA	Virginia	VA
Michigan	MI	Washington	WA
Minnesota	MN	West Virginia	WV
Mississippi	MS	Wisconsin	WI
Missouri	MO	Wyoming	WY

Table 1: Entering Class Average Admitted GPA by Location

State, City	Pharmacy School	Min GPA	Avg Admitted GPA*
AL, Auburn University	Auburn University Harrison	2.50	3.40
AL, Birmingham	Samford University McWhorter	2.75	3.45
AR, Searcy	Harding University	2.50	3.20
AR, Little Rock	University of Arkansas for Medical Sciences	2.50	3.46
AZ, Tucson	University of Arizona	3.00	3.58
AZ, Glendale	Midwestern University - Glendale Campus	2.50	3.10
CA, Los Angeles	West Coast University	2.50	3.28
CA, Elk Grove	California Northstate University	2.60	3.13
CA, Clovis	California Health Sciences University	2.70	3.10
CA, Stockton	University of the Pacific Thomas J. Long	2.70	3.30
CA, Claremont	Keck Graduate Institute	2.75	N/A
CA, Loma Linda	Loma Linda University	2.75	3.34
CA, Vallejo	Touro University California	2.75	3.25
CA, Pomona	Western University of Health Sciences	2.75	3.43
CA, San Francisco	University of California, San Francisco	2.80	3.55
CA, Irvine	Chapman University	3.00	3.30
CA, Fullerton	Marshall B. Ketchum University	3.00	3.00
CA, La Jolla	University of California, San Diego	3.00	3.67
CA, Los Angeles	University of Southern California	3.00	3.50
CO, Denver	Regis University	2.50	3.01
CO, Aurora	University of Colorado	2.50	3.30

State, City	Pharmacy School	Min GPA	Avg Admitted GPA*
CT, Storrs	University of Connecticut	2.50	3.30
CT, Hartford	University of Saint Joseph	2.80	3.10
DC, Washington	Howard University	2.50	3.22
FL, Gainesville	University of Florida	2.50	3.40
FL, Bradenton	Lake Erie College of Osteopathic Medicine - Bradenton Campus	2.70	3.25
FL, Miami	Larkin University	2.70	N/A
FL, Tallahassee	Florida A&M University	2.75	3.28
FL, Fort Lauderdale	Nova Southeastern University	2.75	3.52
FL, West Palm Beach	Palm Beach Atlantic University	2.75	3.20
FL, Tampa	University of South Florida	2.75	3.0-4.0
GA, Suwanee	Philadelphia College of Osteopathic Medicine - Georgia Campus	2.25	3.00
GA, Atlanta	Mercer University	2.50	3.30
GA, Athens	University of Georgia	2.50	3.40
GA, Savannah	South University	2.80	3.27
HI, Hilo	University of Hawaii	2.50	3.10
IA, Iowa City	The University of Iowa	2.75	3.30
IA, Des Moines	Drake University	3.00	N/A
ID, Pocatello	Idaho State University	2.50	3.30
IL, Chicago	Chicago State University	2.50	3.10
IL, Downers Grove	Midwestern University - Downers Grove Campus	2.50	3.20
IL, Schaumburg	Roosevelt University	2.50	3.10

State, City	Pharmacy School	Min GPA	Avg Admitted GPA*
IL, North Chicago	Rosalind Franklin University of Medicine and Science	2.50	3.07
IL, Chicago	University of Illinois at Chicago	2.50	3.40
IL, Edwardsville	Southern Illinois University Edwardsville	2.75	3.65
IN, Fort Wayne	Manchester University	2.50	3.20
IN, Indianapolis	Butler University	3.00	3.40
IN, West Lafayette	Purdue University	3.00	3.40
KS, Lawrence	The University of Kansas	2.50	3.48
KY, Lexington	University of Kentucky	2.50	3-3.6
KY, Louisville	Sullivan University	3.00	3.40
LA, Monroe	The University of Louisiana Monroe	2.50	3.60
LA, New Orleans	Xavier University of Louisiana	2.75	3.30
Lebanon, Byblos	Lebanese American University	2.50	3.20
MA, Worcester	Massachusetts College of Pharmacy and Health Sciences	2.70	3.30
MA, Boston	Massachusetts College of Pharmacy and Health Sciences	3.00	N/A
MA, Boston	Northeastern University	3.00	N/A
MA, Springfield	Western New England University	3.00	3.38
MD, Baltimore	Notre Dame of Maryland University	2.50	3.10
MD, Baltimore	University of Maryland	2.50	3.40
MD, Princess Anne	University of Maryland Eastern Shore	2.50	3.30
ME, Portland	University of New England	2.50	3.10
ME, Bangor	Husson University	2.75	3.30

State, City	Pharmacy School	Min GPA	Avg Admitted GPA*
MI, Big Rapids	Ferris State University	2.50	3.40
MI, Detroit	Wayne State University	2.75	3.60
MI, Ann Arbor	University of Michigan	2.80	3.50
MN, Duluth	University of Minnesota	2.25	3.40
MO, Kansas City	University of Missouri	2.75	3.40
MS, Biloxi	William Carey University	2.50	3.36
MS, University	The University of Mississippi	2.75	3.36
MT, Missoula	University of Montana	2.50	3.30
NC, Buies Creek	Campbell University	2.50	3.34
NC, Chapel Hill	The University of North Carolina (UNC) at Chapel Hill Eshelman	2.50	3.50
NC, High Point	High Point University	2.60	3.20
NC, Hendersonville	Wingate University - Hendersonville	2.75	3.39
NC, Wingate	Wingate University - Wingate	2.75	3.26
ND, Fargo	North Dakota State University	3.00	3.67
NE, Omaha	Creighton University	2.00	3.30
NE, Omaha	University of Nebraska	2.50	3.64
NH, Manchester	Massachusetts College of Pharmacy and Health Sciences - Manchester	2.70	3.30
NJ, Florham Park	Fairleigh Dickinson University	2.75	3.30
NJ, Piscatway	Rutgers, The State University of New Jersey	2.80	3.50
NM, Albuquerque	The University of New Mexico	2.50	3.34
NV, Henderson	Roseman University of Health Sciences	2.80	3.11
NY, Albany	Albany College of Pharmacy and Health Sciences	2.50	3.30

State, City	Pharmacy School	Min GPA	Avg Admitted GPA*
NY, Buffalo	D'Youville College	2.50	3.12
NY, Stony Brook	Stony Brook University	2.50	N/A
NY, New York	Touro College (NY)	2.50	3.28
NY, Binghamton	Binghamton University - SUNY School of Pharmacy and Pharmaceutical Sciences	2.75	3.20
NY, Rochester	St. John Fisher College Wegmans School of Pharmacy	2.75	3.40
NY, Brooklyn	Long Island University Arnold & Marie Schwartz College of Pharmacy and Health Sciences	3.00	3.30
NY, Buffalo	University at Buffalo - SUNY School of Pharmacy and Pharmaceutical Sciences	3.00	3.50
OH, Rootstown	Northeast Ohio Medical University (NEOMED)	2.50	3.20
OH, Columbus	The Ohio State University	2.70	3.46
OH, Cincinnati	University of Cincinnati	2.85	3.30
OH, Cedarville	Cedarville University	3.00	3.35
OH, Findlay	The University of Findlay	3.00	3.30
OH, Toledo	The University of Toledo	3.00	3.60
OK, Weatherford	Southwestern Oklahoma State University	2.50	3.50
OK, Oklahoma City	The University of Oklahoma	2.50	3.64
OR, Hillsboro	Pacific University Oregon	2.70	3.30
OR	Oregon State University (resident 2.75, non-resident 3.0)	2.75	3.50
PA, Wilkes-Barre	Wilkes University Nesbitt School of Pharmacy	2.50	3.44
PA, Erie	Lake Erie College of Osteopathic Medicine - Distance Education Pathway	2.70	3.39
PA, Erie	Lake Erie College of Osteopathic Medicine - Erie Campus	2.70	3.46

State, City	Pharmacy School	Min GPA	Avg Admitted GPA*
PA, Philadelphia	Temple University	2.70	3.10
PA, Philadelphia	Thomas Jefferson University	2.70	3.34
PA, Pittsburgh	Duquesne University	2.90	3.45
PA, Pittsburgh	University of Pittsburgh	3.00	3.50
PA, Philadelphia	University of the Sciences in Philadelphia	3.00	3.40
PR, San Juan	University of Puerto Rico, PR=Puerto Rico	2.75	3.71
SC, Charleston	Medical University of South Carolina	2.50	3.40
SC, Clinton	Presbyterian College	2.50	3.30
SC, Columbia	University of South Carolina	2.50	3.65
SC, Columbia	South University (SC)	2.80	3.27
TN, Memphis	The University of Tennessee	2.00	3.40
TN, Nashville	Belmont University	2.50	3.20
TN, Nashville	Lipscomb University	2.50	3.22
TN, Knoxville	South College (TN)	2.50	3.00
TN, Jackson	Union University	2.50	3.30
TN, Johnson City	East Tennessee State University Bill Gatton	2.70	3.30
TX, El Paso	The University of Texas at El Paso	2.50	3.47
TX, Tyler	The University of Texas at Tyler	2.50	3.23
TX, Houston	University of Houston	2.50	3.54
TX, Fort Worth	University of North Texas Health Science Center System	2.50	3.24
TX, San Antonio	University of the Incarnate Word	2.50	3.25

State, City	Pharmacy School	Min GPA	Avg Admitted GPA*
TX, Kingsville	Texas A&M University	2.75	3.47
TX, Houston	Texas Southern University	2.75	3.39
TX, Austin	The University of Texas at Austin	2.80	3.50
TX, Amarillo	Texas Tech University Health Sciences Center	3.00	3.42
UT, Salt Lake City	University of Utah	3.00	3.50
VA, Oakwood	Appalachian College of Pharmacy	2.50	2.96
VA, Winchester	Shenandoah University	2.50	3.19
VA, Richmond	Virginia Commonwealth University	2.50	3.40
VA, Hampton	Hampton University	2.75	3.20
VT, Colchester	Albany College of Pharmacy and Health Sciences - Colchester	2.50	3.30
WA, Spokane	Washington State University	2.70	3.30
WA, Seattle	University of Washington	2.80	3.47
WI, Milwaukee	Medical College of Wisconsin Pharmacy School	2.00	3.00
WI, Mequon	Concordia University Wisconsin School of Pharmacy	2.75	3.30
WI, Madison	University of Wisconsin	2.80	3.50
WV, Huntington	Marshall University	2.75	3.05
WV, Charleston	University of Charleston	2.75	3.20
WV, Morgantown	West Virginia University	3.00	3.50
WY, Laramie	University of Wyoming	2.80	3.34

*Fall 2018 entering class average admitted GPA

Table 2: Pharmacy Schools by "Minimum GPA to Apply"

State	Pharmacy School Name	Min. GPA to Apply	Avg Admit GPA*
NE	Creighton University	2.00	3.30
TN	The University of Tennessee	2.00	3.40
WI	Medical College of Wisconsin Pharmacy School	2.00	3.00
GA	Philadelphia College of Osteopathic Medicine - Georgia Campus	2.25	3.00
MN	University of Minnesota	2.25	3.40
AL	Auburn University	2.50	3.40
AR	Harding University	2.50	3.20
AR	University of Arkansas for Medical Sciences	2.50	3.46
AZ	Midwestern University - Glendale Campus	2.50	3.10
CA	West Coast University	2.50	3.28
CO	Regis University	2.50	3.01
CO	University of Colorado	2.50	3.30
CT	University of Connecticut	2.50	3.30
DC	Howard University	2.50	3.22
FL	University of Florida	2.50	3.40
GA	Mercer University	2.50	3.30
GA	University of Georgia	2.50	3.40
HI	University of Hawaii	2.50	3.10
ID	Idaho State University	2.50	3.30
IL	Chicago State University	2.50	3.10

State	Pharmacy School Name	Min. GPA to Apply	Avg Admit GPA*
IL	Midwestern University - Downers Grove Campus	2.50	3.20
IL	Roosevelt University	2.50	3.10
IL	Rosalind Franklin University of Medicine and Science	2.50	3.07
IL	University of Illinois at Chicago	2.50	3.40
IN	Manchester University Pharmacy Program	2.50	3.20
KS	The University of Kansas	2.50	3.48
KY	University of Kentucky	2.50	3-3.6
LA	The University of Louisiana	2.50	3.60
Lebanon	Lebanese American University School of Pharmacy	2.50	3.20
MD	Notre Dame of Maryland University	2.50	3.10
MD	University of Maryland	2.50	3.40
MD	University of Maryland Eastern Shore	2.50	3.30
ME	University of New England	2.50	3.10
MI	Ferris State University	2.50	3.40
MS	William Carey University	2.50	3.36
MT	University of Montana	2.50	3.30
NC	Campbell University	2.50	3.34
NC	The University of North Carolina (UNC) at Chapel Hill Eshelman	2.50	3.50
NE	University of Nebraska Medical Center	2.50	3.64
NM	The University of New Mexico Health Sciences Center	2.50	3.34
NY	Albany College of Pharmacy and Health Sciences	2.50	3.30

State	Pharmacy School Name	Min. GPA to Apply	Avg Admit GPA*
NY	D'Youville College	2.50	3.12
NY	Stony Brook University	2.50	N/A
NY	Touro College (NY)	2.50	3.28
OH	Northeast Ohio Medical University (NEOMED)	2.50	3.20
OK	Southwestern Oklahoma State University	2.50	3.50
OK	The University of Oklahoma	2.50	3.64
PA	Wilkes University	2.50	3.44
SC	Medical University of South Carolina	2.50	3.40
SC	Presbyterian College	2.50	3.30
SC	University of South Carolina	2.50	3.65
TN	Belmont University	2.50	3.20
TN	Lipscomb University	2.50	3.22
TN	South College (TN)	2.50	3.00
TN	Union University	2.50	3.30
TX	The University of Texas at El Paso	2.50	3.47
TX	The University of Texas at Tyler	2.50	3.23
TX	University of Houston	2.50	3.54
TX	University of North Texas Health Science Center System	2.50	3.24
TX	University of the Incarnate Word	2.50	3.25
VA	Appalachian College of Pharmacy	2.50	2.96
VA	Shenandoah University	2.50	3.19
VA	Virginia Commonwealth University	2.50	3.40

State	Pharmacy School Name	Min. GPA to Apply	Avg Admit GPA*
VT	Albany College of Pharmacy and Health Sciences - Colchester	2.50	3.30
CA	California Northstate University	2.60	3.13
NC	High Point University	2.60	3.20
CA	California Health Sciences University	2.70	3.10
CA	University of the Pacific	2.70	3.30
FL	Lake Erie College of Osteopathic Medicine - Bradenton Campus	2.70	3.25
FL	Larkin University	2.70	N/A
MA	Massachusetts College of Pharmacy and Health Sciences - Worcester	2.70	3.30
NH	Massachusetts College of Pharmacy and Health Sciences - Manchester	2.70	3.30
OH	The Ohio State University	2.70	3.46
OR	Pacific University Oregon	2.70	3.30
PA	Lake Erie College of Osteopathic Medicine - Distance Education Pathway	2.70	3.39
PA	Lake Erie College of Osteopathic Medicine - Erie Campus	2.70	3.46
PA	Temple University	2.70	3.10
PA	Thomas Jefferson University	2.70	3.34
TN	East Tennessee State University	2.70	3.30
WA	Washington State University	2.70	3.30
AL	Samford University McWhorter	2.75	3.45
CA	Keck Graduate Institute	2.75	N/A
CA	Loma Linda University	2.75	3.34
CA	Touro University California	2.75	3.25

State	Pharmacy School Name	Min. GPA to Apply	Avg Admit GPA*
CA	Western University of Health Sciences	2.75	3.43
FL	Florida A&M University	2.75	3.28
FL	Nova Southeastern University	2.75	3.52
FL	Palm Beach Atlantic University	2.75	3.20
FL	University of South Florida	2.75	3.0-4.0
IA	The University of Iowa	2.75	3.30
IL	Southern Illinois University	2.75	3.65
LA	Xavier University of Louisiana	2.75	3.30
ME	Husson University	2.75	3.30
MI	Wayne State University	2.75	3.60
MO	University of Missouri	2.75	3.40
MS	The University of Mississippi	2.75	3.36
NC	Wingate University - Hendersonville	2.75	3.39
NC	Wingate University - Wingate	2.75	3.26
NJ	Fairleigh Dickinson University	2.75	3.30
NY	Binghamton University - SUNY School of Pharmacy and Pharmaceutical Sciences	2.75	3.20
NY	St. John Fisher College	2.75	3.40
OR	Oregon State University (resident 2.75, non-resident 3.0)	2.75	3.50
PR	University of Puerto Rico (PR=Puerto Rico)	2.75	3.71
TX	Texas A&M University	2.75	3.47
TX	Texas Southern University	2.75	3.39
VA	Hampton University	2.75	3.20

State	Pharmacy School Name	Min. GPA to Apply	Avg Admit GPA*
WI	Concordia University	2.75	3.30
WV	Marshall University	2.75	3.05
WV	University of Charleston	2.75	3.20
CA	University of California, San Francisco	2.80	3.55
CT	University of Saint Joseph	2.80	3.10
GA	South University (GA)	2.80	3.27
MI	University of Michigan	2.80	3.50
NJ	Rutgers, The State University of New Jersey	2.80	3.50
NV	Roseman University of Health Sciences	2.80	3.11
SC	South University (SC)	2.80	3.27
TX	The University of Texas at Austin	2.80	3.50
WA	University of Washington	2.80	3.47
WI	University of Wisconsin	2.80	3.50
WY	University of Wyoming	2.80	3.34
OH	University of Cincinnati	2.85	3.30
PA	Duquesne University	2.90	3.45
AZ	University of Arizona	3.00	3.58
CA	Chapman University	3.00	3.30
CA	Marshall B. Ketchum University	3.00	3.00
CA	University of California, San Diego	3.00	3.67
CA	University of Southern California	3.00	3.50
IA	Drake University	3.00	N/A

State	Pharmacy School Name	Min. GPA to Apply	Avg Admit GPA*
IN	Butler University	3.00	3.40
IN	Purdue University	3.00	3.40
KY	Sullivan University	3.00	3.40
MA	Massachusetts College of Pharmacy and Health Sciences - Boston	3.00	N/A
MA	Northeastern University	3.00	N/A
MA	Western New England University	3.00	3.38
ND	North Dakota State University	3.00	3.67
NY	Long Island University	3.00	3.30
NY	University at Buffalo - SUNY School of Pharmacy and Pharmaceutical Sciences	3.00	3.50
OH	Cedarville University	3.00	3.35
OH	The University of Findlay	3.00	3.30
OH	The University of Toledo	3.00	3.60
PA	University of Pittsburgh	3.00	3.50
PA	University of the Sciences in Philadelphia	3.00	3.40
TX	Texas Tech University Health Sciences Center	3.00	3.42
UT	University of Utah	3.00	3.50
WV	West Virginia University	3.00	3.50

*Fall 2018 entering class average admitted GPA

Table 3: Lowest to Highest Average Admitted GPA of Entering Class

State	Pharmacy School Name	Min GPA to Apply	Avg Admit GPA*
VA	Appalachian College of Pharmacy	2.50	2.96
WI	Medical College of Wisconsin Pharmacy School	2.00	3.00
GA	Philadelphia College of Osteopathic Medicine - Georgia Campus	2.25	3.00
TN	South College (TN)	2.50	3.00
CA	Marshall B. Ketchum University	3.00	3.00
CO	Regis University	2.50	3.01
WV	Marshall University	2.75	3.05
IL	Rosalind Franklin University of Medicine and Science	2.50	3.07
AZ	Midwestern University - Glendale Campus	2.50	3.10
HI	University of Hawaii at Hilo	2.50	3.10
IL	Chicago State University	2.50	3.10
IL	Roosevelt University	2.50	3.10
MD	Notre Dame of Maryland University	2.50	3.10
ME	University of New England	2.50	3.10
CA	California Health Sciences University	2.70	3.10
PA	Temple University	2.70	3.10
CT	University of Saint Joseph	2.80	3.10
NV	Roseman University of Health Sciences	2.80	3.11
NY	D'Youville College	2.50	3.12
CA	California Northstate University	2.60	3.13
VA	Shenandoah University	2.50	3.19

State	Pharmacy School Name	Min GPA to Apply	Avg Admit GPA*
AR	Harding University	2.50	3.20
IL	Midwestern University - Downers Grove Campus	2.50	3.20
IN	Manchester University	2.50	3.20
Lebanon	Lebanese American University	2.50	3.20
OH	Northeast Ohio Medical University (NEOMED)	2.50	3.20
TN	Belmont University	2.50	3.20
NC	High Point University	2.60	3.20
FL	Palm Beach Atlantic University	2.75	3.20
NY	Binghamton University	2.75	3.20
VA	Hampton University	2.75	3.20
WV	University of Charleston	2.75	3.20
DC	Howard University	2.50	3.22
TN	Lipscomb University	2.50	3.22
TX	The University of Texas at Tyler	2.50	3.23
TX	University of North Texas Health Science Center System	2.50	3.24
TX	University of the Incarnate Word	2.50	3.25
FL	Lake Erie College of Osteopathic Medicine - Bradenton Campus	2.70	3.25
CA	Touro University California	2.75	3.25
NC	Wingate University - Wingate	2.75	3.26
GA	South University (GA)	2.80	3.27
SC	South University (SC)	2.80	3.27

State	Pharmacy School Name	Min GPA to Apply	Avg Admit GPA*
CA	West Coast University	2.50	3.28
NY	Touro College (NY)	2.50	3.28
FL	Florida A&M University	2.75	3.28
NE	Creighton University	2.00	3.30
CO	University of Colorado	2.50	3.30
CT	University of Connecticut	2.50	3.30
GA	Mercer University	2.50	3.30
ID	Idaho State University	2.50	3.30
MD	University of Maryland Eastern Shore	2.50	3.30
MT	University of Montana	2.50	3.30
NY	Albany College of Pharmacy and Health Sciences	2.50	3.30
SC	Presbyterian College	2.50	3.30
TN	Union University	2.50	3.30
VT	Albany College of Pharmacy and Health Sciences - Colchester	2.50	3.30
CA	University of the Pacific	2.70	3.30
MA	Massachusetts College of Pharmacy and Health Sciences - Worcester	2.70	3.30
NH	Massachusetts College of Pharmacy and Health Sciences - Manchester	2.70	3.30
OR	Pacific University Oregon	2.70	3.30
TN	East Tennessee State University	2.70	3.30
WA	Washington State University	2.70	3.30
IA	The University of Iowa	2.75	3.30

State	Pharmacy School Name	Min GPA to Apply	Avg Admit GPA*
LA	Xavier University of Louisiana	2.75	3.30
ME	Husson University	2.75	3.30
NJ	Fairleigh Dickinson University	2.75	3.30
WI	Concordia University Wisconsin	2.75	3.30
OH	University of Cincinnati	2.85	3.30
CA	Chapman University	3.00	3.30
NY	Long Island University	3.00	3.30
OH	The University of Findlay	3.00	3.30
NC	Campbell University	2.50	3.34
NM	The University of New Mexico Health Sciences Center	2.50	3.34
PA	Thomas Jefferson University	2.70	3.34
CA	Loma Linda University	2.75	3.34
WY	University of Wyoming	2.80	3.34
OH	Cedarville University	3.00	3.35
MS	William Carey University	2.50	3.36
MS	The University of Mississippi	2.75	3.36
MA	Western New England University	3.00	3.38
PA	Lake Erie College of Osteopathic Medicine - Distance Education Pathway	2.70	3.39
NC	Wingate University - Hendersonville	2.75	3.39
TX	Texas Southern University	2.75	3.39
TN	The University of Tennessee	2.00	3.40
MN	University of Minnesota	2.25	3.40

State	Pharmacy School Name	Min GPA to Apply	Avg Admit GPA*
AL	Auburn University Harrison	2.50	3.40
FL	University of Florida	2.50	3.40
GA	University of Georgia	2.50	3.40
IL	University of Illinois at Chicago	2.50	3.40
MD	University of Maryland	2.50	3.40
MI	Ferris State University	2.50	3.40
SC	Medical University of South Carolina	2.50	3.40
VA	Virginia Commonwealth University	2.50	3.40
MO	University of Missouri-Kansas City	2.75	3.40
NY	St. John Fisher College	2.75	3.40
IN	Butler University	3.00	3.40
IN	Purdue University	3.00	3.40
KY	Sullivan University	3.00	3.40
PA	University of the Sciences in Philadelphia	3.00	3.40
TX	Texas Tech University Health Sciences Center	3.00	3.42
CA	Western University of Health Sciences	2.75	3.43
PA	Wilkes University Nesbitt	2.50	3.44
AL	Samford University McWhorter	2.75	3.45
PA	Duquesne University	2.90	3.45
AR	University of Arkansas for Medical Sciences	2.50	3.46
OH	The Ohio State University	2.70	3.46
PA	Lake Erie College of Osteopathic Medicine - Erie Campus	2.70	3.46

State	Pharmacy School Name	Min GPA to Apply	Avg Admit GPA*
TX	The University of Texas at El Paso	2.50	3.47
TX	Texas A&M University	2.75	3.47
WA	University of Washington	2.80	3.47
KS	The University of Kansas	2.50	3.48
NC	The University of North Carolina (UNC) at Chapel Hill	2.50	3.50
OK	Southwestern Oklahoma State University	2.50	3.50
OR	Oregon State University (resident 2.75, non-resident 3.0)	2.75	3.50
MI	University of Michigan	2.80	3.50
NJ	Rutgers, The State University of New Jersey	2.80	3.50
TX	The University of Texas at Austin	2.80	3.50
WI	University of Wisconsin	2.80	3.50
CA	University of Southern California	3.00	3.50
NY	University at Buffalo - SUNY School of Pharmacy and Pharmaceutical Sciences	3.00	3.50
PA	University of Pittsburgh	3.00	3.50
UT	University of Utah	3.00	3.50
WV	West Virginia University	3.00	3.50
FL	Nova Southeastern University	2.75	3.52
TX	University of Houston	2.50	3.54
CA	University of California, San Francisco	2.80	3.55
AZ	University of Arizona	3.00	3.58
LA	The University of Louisiana	2.50	3.60

State	Pharmacy School Name	Min GPA to Apply	Avg Admit GPA*
MI	Wayne State University	2.75	3.60
OH	The University of Toledo	3.00	3.60
NE	University of Nebraska Medical Center	2.50	3.64
OK	The University of Oklahoma	2.50	3.64
SC	University of South Carolina	2.50	3.65
IL	Southern Illinois University Edwardsville	2.75	3.65
CA	University of California, San Diego	3.00	3.67
ND	North Dakota State University	3.00	3.67
PR	University of Puerto Rico (PR=Puerto Rico)	2.75	3.71
FL	University of South Florida	2.75	3.0-4.0
KY	University of Kentucky	2.50	3-3.6
NY	Stony Brook University	2.50	N/A
FL	Larkin University	2.70	N/A
CA	Keck Graduate Institute	2.75	N/A
IA	Drake University	3.00	N/A
MA	Massachusetts College of Pharmacy and Health Sciences - Boston	3.00	N/A
MA	Northeastern University	3.00	N/A

*Fall 2018 entering class average admitted GPA

Pharmacy College Admission Test (PCAT)

The Pharmacy College Admission Test (PCAT) is not a mandatory exam like the MCAT for pre-med students. Most pharmacy schools (about 85%)[1] do require a PCAT score and therefore having it would enable you to apply to a lot more schools. However, there are a decent number of schools, listed below, that do not require PCAT. [2]

The PCAT is a specialized test that helps identify qualified applicants to pharmacy colleges. It measures general academic ability and scientific knowledge necessary for starting pharmacy school. More specifically, the exam tests your foundational scientific knowledge, math, verbal, reading comprehension, and writing skills and overall critical thinking.

The PCAT is administered in a computer-based test (CBT) format. For the 2018–2019 testing cycle, administration of the PCAT will occur on various dates in the months of July, September, October, November, January and February. As there are many PCAT preparation courses and books available, we recommend that you check out our websites (pharmacyinterview.com or reshapethemind.com) under "resources" should you plan on taking it.

Remember, the PCAT is but one piece of a really large puzzle. Your PCAT score does not define who you are, what you stand for or your true potential. You are much more than a score. While your PCAT score gives the school an idea of your academic abilities, there is so much it does not tell the school, such as your passion for pharmacy, your commitment to help the underserved, your leadership potential, your unique perspective on patient care, your ability to make a positive impact on the health of future patients, your unquenchable thirst for knowledge and your desire to be a lifelong learner, your vision for the future of pharmacy, your compassion to serve the community through meaningful extracurricular activities, your interest in teaching and sharing your knowledge, your willingness to persevere through tough times, etc.

In the chart below, you will find the average PCAT percentile for the recent admitted class. You can compare your own PCAT scores and gauge where you stand.

Table 4: Average PCAT percentile for Admitted Class

State, City	Pharmacy School	PCAT percentile
AL, Auburn University	Auburn University Harrison	62
AL, Birmingham	Samford University McWhorter	60
AR, Searcy	Harding University	60
AR, Little Rock	University of Arkansas for Medical Sciences	67
AZ, Tucson	University of Arizona	68.5
AZ, Glendale	Midwestern University - Glendale Campus	50
CA, San Francisco	University of California, San Francisco	89/431 mean composite score
CO, Denver	Regis University	30-99
CO, Aurora	University of Colorado	Unknown
CT, Storrs	University of Connecticut	Unknown
CT, Hartford	University of Saint Joseph	Unknown
FL, Gainesville	University of Florida	50 to 88 (25 to 75 percentile)
FL, Miami	Larkin University	Unknown
FL, Fort Lauderdale	Nova Southeastern University	Unknown
FL, West Palm Beach	Palm Beach Atlantic University	72
FL, Tampa	University of South Florida	Unknown

State, City	Pharmacy School	PCAT percentile
GA, Suwanee	Philadelphia College of Osteopathic Medicine - Georgia Campus	Unknown
GA, Atlanta	Mercer University	66
GA, Athens	University of Georgia	80
IA, Iowa City	The University of Iowa	70
IA, Des Moines	Drake University	50
IL, Chicago	Chicago State University	Unknown
IL, Downers Grove	Midwestern University - Downers Grove Campus	50
IL, Schaumburg	Roosevelt University	57
IL, North Chicago	Rosalind Franklin University of Medicine and Science	48
IL, Chicago	University of Illinois at Chicago	Unknown
IL, Edwardsville	Southern Illinois University Edwardsville	Unknown
KS, Lawrence	The University of Kansas	65
KY, Lexington	University of Kentucky	78
LA, Monroe	The University of Louisiana Monroe	Unknown
MA, Boston	Northeastern University	Unknown
MD, Baltimore	Notre Dame of Maryland University	50
MD, Baltimore	University of Maryland	70
MD, Princess Anne	University of Maryland Eastern Shore	35 - 65
ME, Portland	University of New England	Unknown
ME, Bangor	Husson University	55
MI, Big Rapids	Ferris State University	73
MI, Detroit	Wayne State University	75

State, City	Pharmacy School	PCAT percentile
MI, Ann Arbor	University of Michigan	75
MN, Duluth	University of Minnesota	82
MO, Kansas City	University of Missouri	65
MS, University	The University of Mississippi	408 - 410 mean composite score
MT, Missoula	University of Montana	68
NC, Buies Creek	Campbell University	70
NC, Chapel Hill	The University of North Carolina (UNC) at Chapel Hill	55
NC, High Point	High Point University	65
NC, Hendersonville	Wingate University - Hendersonville	Unknown (not required if GPA 3.0 or above)
NC, Wingate	Wingate University - Wingate	55
ND, Fargo	North Dakota State University	63
NE, Omaha	Creighton University	66
NE, Omaha	University of Nebraska	66
NJ, Florham Park	Fairleigh Dickinson University	Unknown
NJ, Piscatway	Rutgers, The State University of New Jersey	Unknown
NM, Albuquerque	The University of New Mexico	54
NV, Henderson	Roseman University of Health Sciences	Unknown (waived if you have a Bachelor degree)
NY, Albany	Albany College of Pharmacy and Health Sciences	51
NY, Buffalo	D'Youville College	Unknown
NY, Stony Brook	Stony Brook University	Unknown
NY, Binghamton	Binghamton University	Unknown (above national average is considered highly competitive)
NY, Brooklyn	Long Island University	Unknown
NY, Buffalo	University at Buffalo	50

State, City	Pharmacy School	PCAT percentile
OH, Columbus	The Ohio State University	80 - 85
OH, Cincinnati	University of Cincinnati	71
OH, Cedarville	Cedarville University	Unknown
OH, Toledo	The University of Toledo	8 - 95
OK, Weatherford	Southwestern Oklahoma State University	63
OK, Oklahoma City	The University of Oklahoma	Unknown
PA, Wilkes-Barre	Wilkes University Nesbitt School of Pharmacy	Unknown
PA, Philadelphia	Temple University	Unknown
PA, Philadelphia	Thomas Jefferson University	70
PA, Pittsburgh	Duquesne University	33
PA, Pittsburgh	University of Pittsburgh	81
PA, Philadelphia	University of the Sciences in Philadelphia	Unknown
PR, San Juan	University of Puerto Rico, PR=Puerto Rico	Unknown
SC, Charleston	Medical University of South Carolina	68
SC, Clinton	Presbyterian College	Unknown
SC, Columbia	University of South Carolina	68
TN, Nashville	Belmont University	61
TN, Jackson	Union University	Unknown
TX, El Paso	The University of Texas at El Paso	Unknown
TX, Tyler	The University of Texas at Tyler	38
TX, Houston	University of Houston	78
TX, Fort Worth	University of North Texas Health Science Center System	70
TX, San Antonio	University of the Incarnate Word	57

State, City	Pharmacy School	PCAT percentile
TX, Kingsville	Texas A&M University	Unknown
TX, Houston	Texas Southern University	48
TX, Austin	The University of Texas at Austin	Unknown
TX, Amarillo	Texas Tech University Health Sciences Center	73
UT, Salt Lake City	University of Utah	84
VA, Oakwood	Appalachian College of Pharmacy	50
VA, Winchester	Shenandoah University	52
VA, Richmond	Virginia Commonwealth University	Unknown
VA, Hampton	Hampton University	82
VT, Colchester	Albany College of Pharmacy and Health Sciences - Colchester	Unknown
WA, Seattle	University of Washington	87
WI, Milwaukee	Medical College of Wisconsin Pharmacy School	Unknown
WI, Mequon	Concordia University Wisconsin	68
WI, Madison	University of Wisconsin	81
WV, Huntington	Marshall University	50
WV, Charleston	University of Charleston	51
WV, Morgantown	West Virginia University	51
WY, Laramie	University of Wyoming	Unknown

Table 5: Schools That Do Not Require the PCAT Score[3]

State	Pharmacy School
California	California Health Sciences University
	California Northstate University
	Keck Graduate Institute
	Loma Linda University
	Marshall B Ketchum University
	Touro University California
	University of California, San Diego
	University of Southern California
	University of the Pacific
	West Coast University
	Western University of Health Sciences
Florida	Florida A&M University
	Lake Erie College of Osteopathic medicine - Bradenton Campus
Georgia	South University
Hawaii	University of Hawaii at Hilo
Idaho	Idaho State University
Indiana	Butler University
	Manchester University
	Purdue University
Kentucky	Sullivan University
Louisiana	Xavier University of Louisiana

Massachusetts	Massachusetts College of Pharmacy and Health Sciences - Boston, MA
	Massachusetts College of Pharmacy and Health Sciences - Worcester, MA
	Western New England University
Mississippi	William Carey University
New Hampshire	Massachusetts College of Pharmacy and Health Sciences - Manchester
New York	St. John's University
	Touro College - College of Pharmacy (NY)
Ohio	Northeast Ohio Medical University
	Ohio Northern University
	The University of Findlay
Oregon	Oregon State University
	Pacific University Oregon
Pennsylvania	Lake Erie College of Osteopathic Medicine – Distance Education Pathway
	Lake Erie College of Osteopathic Medicine - Erie Campus
Rhode Island	The University of Rhode Island
South Carolina	South University
South Dakota	South Dakota State University
Tennessee	East Tennessee State University
Washington	Washington State University
Washington DC	Howard University

Pharmacy-Related Work Experience

It's no secret; applicants with pharmacy-related work experience have a higher chance of getting accepted into pharmacy school. Think of it like a job interview. If you are an owner of a coffee shop, are you more likely to hire a seasoned barista or a plumber? By finding pharmacy-related work, you're demonstrating to your dream pharmacy school that you're ready to make a serious career commitment.

You might find yourself wondering, "But how do I get pharmacy work experience? It's not like there are just entry-level jobs for pre-pharmacy students lying around."

There are several opportunities to gain pharmacy-related work experience and some of them might seem surprising. Remember, pharmacy schools aren't expecting that every applicant will come in ready to be a pharmacist right away; they want to see that you have a strong interest in the pharmacy field as a whole. So, for example, you might volunteer at a medical clinic or hospital or spend a summer as an intern at a bioscience firm.

What kinds of experiences do pharmacy schools look for?

Pharmacy Technician

A pharmacy technician position is the most relevant, hands-on way to gain practical pharmacy experience. Think of it as the gold standard of pharmacy-related experience—not only are you working under a licensed pharmacist but you're directly working with medication, patients, and care providers on a daily basis. Whether it's measuring out prescriptions or interacting with a patient, you're out there getting a true taste of what it's like to be a community pharmacist and, in turn, relevant, valuable experience that directly applies to your future pharmacy studies.

So why doesn't everyone take this route? For one, pharmacy technicians require professional certification and/or licensing. Prospective pharmacy technicians need to take the Pharmacy Technician Certification Exam (PTCE), pass it, and then apply for their pharmacy technician license, and that's **before** applying for the pharmacy technician position itself. Becoming a fully certified and employable pharmacy technician requires anywhere from a few months to a year and is a full-time position on its own. As a result, while we personally believe that being a pharmacy technician offers the strongest relatable pharmacy experience, we also recognize that this isn't a realistic option for everyone. Volunteering in a pharmacy, shadowing a pharmacist or working a cashier or clerk in the pharmacy can also provide valuable experiences that you can leverage in your personal statement or admissions interview.

Pharmacy-related Experiences

Think about experiences you've had that motivated you to become a pharmacist and craft the top three to four into convincing, defining moments in your quest to become a pharmacist. One good example a student used was witnessing a heart attack incident that happened to one of her coworkers, whose life was saved by an emergency drug, nitroglycerin. The student realized how much of a difference a single medication can make and explained to the admissions officer how that realization sparked her ambition to pursue pharmacy as a lifelong career.

Additionally, seek out opportunities that interact with medicine in some way or another. Here's a quick brainstorm to help you get started:

- Volunteer or work with relief efforts
- Volunteer or work at a hospital
- Work as an assistant in a medical office/clinic
- Do some independent scientific research and publish it!

- Volunteer at nursing homes
- Any other opportunities that allow you to serve patients and witness the importance of medication compliance

List companies/medical facilities/public resources that provide treatment or medicine in some shape or form and find an opportunity for yourself. Healthcare is everywhere in multiple shapes and forms—there are numerous opportunities to gain experience in a patient-focused care environment.

Students with pharmacy experience demonstrate the following key qualities pharmacy schools are looking for:

- Interest in the profession
- A general understanding of medications and the healthcare system
- Knowledge of their career options

Letters of Recommendation

When it comes to your pharmacy school application, having strong letters of recommendation is a must. At least two letters of recommendation* will be required as part of the application.

*Please note that hereafter the word "recommendation" will be referred to as "rec" in this chapter.

Applicants often make the mistake of assuming that a). a letter of rec will always be "good" and b). a simple request for a letter of rec is all the referee needs. Remember, **there are bad letters of rec and they can and will break your chances of being accepted.** Letters of rec give admission officers insight into your personal strengths, weaknesses, accomplishments, and context that cannot be gleaned from your transcripts or test scores. A strong letter of rec should positively reflect your social skills as well as how others perceive you.

Requirements

Rec letter requirements vary from school to school. Some schools will not consider your application without a rec letter from a pharmacist and others (e.g. Loma Linda University) require a letter from a pastor, clergy or spiritual advisor. Make sure to thoroughly research and follow each school's specific requirements or you run the risk that your application will be considered incomplete, wasting both your time and your application fees.

Who should I ask to write my rec letters?

Make sure you have letters from at least one pharmacist and one faculty member. With this in mind, you should start cultivating good relationships with these target professionals as soon as possible.

Additionally, as the individuals who are recommending you are often busy, it's advisable to draft a letter of rec for them to review and sign. Make sure to carefully review and verify that the letter is grammatically correct, factually accurate, and meets all of your school's requirements prior to asking your referees to review it as they may not read it as closely as you will.

The Four-Step Recommendation Letter Strategy

1. Pick referees who know you well and care about student success
2. Provide your referees with plenty of time and reference materials
3. Give all submission instructions and deadlines
4. Stay in touch with your referees

Step 1: Pick referees who know you well and care about student success

It is pointless to ask a referee who knows you well but couldn't care less about whether you get accepted into a pharmacy school or not. Therefore, you have to choose your referees wisely.

Professors

Before you even apply to pharmacy school or any graduate level program, start cultivating relationships with certain professors whom you think would be willing to write you a recommendation. Typically, you want to pick professors who know you well on both an academic and a personal basis, meaning they have seen both your academic achievements and your interpersonal skills as well. Ask yourself the following: Have they seen you give a presentation? Were you an active participant in their class? Have they seen you interact with your peers? Have you done a project with this professor? Were you a teaching assistant (TA)? If you don't have any relationships like the ones described above, proactively seek out those opportunities.

If you are already in the process of applying to pharmacy schools and do not have any of these experiences, nor the time to obtain these experiences, we recommend making an appointment with the professor of your choice (preferably a class you did well in) to chit chat and talk about your goals. You can then simply bring up the idea of a letter of recommendation and see where the conversation goes. Professors typically want the best for their students and will sometimes ask for your personal statement, your grades and other supporting documents to help write the best letter for you. Always be prepared and organized to achieve the most efficient and smooth experience. Extra brownie points if you prepare those documents ahead of time to hand over as soon as they agree.

Pharmacy Manager/Staff Pharmacist

To make your application stand out, it is imperative to cultivate good relationships with a pharmacy manager or a staff pharmacist from your work or volunteer experiences. If you work as a pharmacy technician, asking your pharmacy manager or a staff pharmacist to write a letter is a good idea. Having someone in the field of pharmacy to vouch for your potential as a future pharmacist will make you a distinct candidate. Make sure that the pharmacist you ask to write your letter truly cares about your success and sincerely believes that you are a good fit for the profession.

Academic Counselor

Your school academic counselor is another possible option. If you have a counselor whom you meet with regularly throughout your undergraduate/graduate career and who cares deeply about student success, don't be afraid to ask if s/he can write you a strong letter of recommendation. You always want to approach the counselor early, preferably a year ahead, to hold a substantial conversation about your interests and goals. Students usually don't see their counselors more than two or three times per year, so make appointments early and avoid cramming visits during the semester you need their letter, otherwise you appear desperate and unorganized. Don't be that person.

Other good referees include program coordinators or medical relief effort personnel.

Step 2: Provide your referees with plenty of time and reference materials

Be kind to the hand that feeds you and be extremely kind to the writer of your rec letter. Extend the common courtesy of giving your referees at least three months before the due date to write your letters. Rushing them will only result in a mediocre if not a negative recommendation letter. Provide a rec letter reference packet for them. The reference packet should include an academic transcript, your resume (listing your extracurricular activities, work experience, volunteer/leadership positions, research experience, awards/honors, etc.), a past-graded paper/project, your personal statements, and a sample letter of recommendation you wrote from their perspective (this is extremely useful for busy referees). Give them the tools they need and be extremely accommodating.

The sample letter of recommendation should be professional, well-crafted, and relevant to your relationship with the referee. Spend a good deal of time on it since there is the possibility that your referee will simply copy and paste the whole thing and sign it.

Treat your referee well. Are they hungry? Grab them a nice gourmet chicken pesto sandwich. Are they thirsty? Get them a bottle of some fancy sparkling water (the kind that comes in a glass bottle). Remember, THEY are doing YOU a big, fat favor that **they are not getting paid for.** A $8.99 sandwich is a small price to pay for the boost they're giving your $615 pharmacy school application (assuming you apply to nine schools).

It also doesn't hurt that these actions make you stand out amongst all the other rec letters they're probably writing for other students. Just saying.

Step 3: Give all submission instructions and deadlines

Clear instructions as to when, where, and how to submit the letters must be given to your referees. Use calendar reminders on your phone to send deadline reminders to them. While most schools will accept letters via PharmCAS, some require letters to be sent directly to the schools. Provide properly addressed, typed, and stamped envelopes to your referees if the letters must be mailed to the school. Since you will likely be applying with PharmCAS, feel free to use the template we've written for you below:

--- Sample Template ---

Letter Submission Instructions on PharmCAS

You will receive an email from PharmCAS with login instructions for the Evaluator Portal. Once you have finished writing the letter of recommendation, you can submit it to PharmCAS online via the "Letters by Liaison" Evaluator Portal. It is a two-part process:

- Part I: Complete questions and evaluation ratings via the Evaluator Portal.
- Part II: Upload letter of reference via the Evaluator Portal.

PharmCAS emails are sometimes caught in spam or junk folders. Therefore, please contact me if you do not receive their email.

---End of Template---

Always include a specific deadline in your instructions. We recommend you select a date that is at least three months before your earliest deadline so that if any of your preferred referees fail to submit the letter(s) on time, you'll still have some time to follow up or to seek other referees.

Remember that you need to submit an evaluation (also known as a Letter of Recommendation) request on PharmCAS to your referee. The instructions are on PharmCAS. **It is your responsibility to ensure that evaluation requests are received and completed on time.**

Step 4: Stay in touch with your referees

Regardless of how insanely busy you are with school work, stay in touch with your referees. After submitting your application, write each of them a thank-you note expressing your appreciation for their support. Keep them posted with any major updates on your application status, such as receiving an interview or acceptance letter. Maintaining a close and positive relationship with your referees will pave the way if you happen to need more favors from them in the future.

Personal Statements

This is probably the most important section of your entire application besides your GPA. Even if you are a good writer, start writing your draft **months** in advance. You'd be surprised by how difficult it is to produce a high-quality essay.

There are students who start planning it one year in advance. They write down moments that inspired them during their encounters with pharmacists, being in pharmacies, and volunteer experiences in the pharmacy. It is extremely important to come across as genuine. Talk about real experiences and real events. Admissions officers read hundreds of applications every year, so they're pros at sniffing out fake, made-up stories. Be genuine, infuse your personal statement with emotion and conviction, and your story will shine.

In this section, we have included real, unedited examples of personal statements sent to pharmacy schools by students who are now pharmacists. These are PharmCAS essays and supplemental essays. You may find grammar errors as these are real drafts! The names and companies used in these essays have been edited for confidentiality purposes.

Candidate #1

GPA 3.8, accepted into UCSF, UCSD, USC, UOP.

PharmCAS essay: **Your Personal Essay should address why you selected pharmacy as a career and How the Doctor of Pharmacy degree relates to your immediate and long-term professional goals. Describe how your personal, educational, and professional background will help you achieve your goals.**

"What do you like best about being a Pharmacist?" I asked Dr. Smith curiously. Dr. Smith was my mentor from the University XYZ Health & Medical Professions Preparation Program. He looked at me straight in the eye, and responded, "Being able to save lives." I was surprised by his simple answer, yet I got a strong sense that he really meant what he said from the serious expression that normally did not appear on his gentle face. As we continued our discussion, I began to understand what Dr. Smith meant and why there is such a strong need for caring pharmacists in healthcare.

Dr. Smith explained to me that a pharmacist is the last line of defense in the Medical team, since he or she is the last person to handle the medication before it is given to the patients. I learned that a pharmacist who makes one positive change in medical therapy or catches one prescription error is able to impact many lives. At the end of our conversation, I felt greatly inspired and moved by the genuine care Dr. Smith had for people.

An advice Dr. Smith gave me was to always be overly cautious when verifying the legitimacy of a prescription. I later realized the significance of his advice when I worked at PharmaCompany, a pharmaceutical company which manufactures drug products for human use. I was trained to document data thoroughly and use reagents efficiently so that nothing was wasted. I prepared a variety of chemical solutions, some which took up to 8 hours to make and used up to 3 bottles of reagents where each bottle cost over a hundred dollars to manufacture. I learned that a small mistake such as forgetting to put the expiration date on a prepared solution label would cause the entire solution to be discarded. From working at PharmaCompany, I learned firsthand the immense costs and the extensive work that goes into developing a drug. I also gained significant insight into the struggles it takes to prepare a pharmaceutical product. Most importantly, the experience has trained me to be extremely attentive to details. This unique experience is especially valuable to me because as a future pharmacist, my every action will have a direct impact on the health of a patient.

My passion for pharmacy grew stronger from taking Pharmacology taught by Dr. John Winchester. While I was taking this class, the relevance of medicine struck me personally. Having had the good fortune of being a healthy individual, I have never needed to take any prescribed medication, and therefore have not experienced a drug's power to relieve a person's discomfort or pain. Coincidently, during the week that I learned about anti-allergy medications in Pharmacology class, I experienced my first allergic reaction. I was in extreme pain and agony, as gigantic red rashes spread all over my body. I felt an overwhelming sense of relief a few hours after taking Zyrtec as the rashes slowly disappeared. Two days after my allergic reaction, I happened to learn about Zyrtec in class. It was a fantastic feeling to know the exact mechanism to the drug that I was taking. I thought about how remarkable it is that a small molecule is able to change the whole course of a disease, and relieve the pain that a person is suffering from. Personally experiencing the effects of a drug has made me realize the significance of pharmaceutical agents in improving the quality of patients' lives.

From talking to many pharmacists, I have learned that one of the best parts about the job is the different interactions you have with people. Teaching an organic chemistry workshop has cultivated my passion for working with others. The experience has taught me how to explain complicated concepts clearly so that students can understand. I also learned how to make students feel comfortable around me through initiating friendly conversations, and showing interest in their concerns. The most memorable moment for me was when my students came up to me to give me hugs after my last workshop. I felt then that all my hard work was worth it. When I become a pharmacist, I will use my strong communication skills to better understand my patients' needs and educate them on the importance of their medication.

As a future pharmacist, I am ready to commit to the lifelong learning that comes with the profession. I plan to mentor future pre-pharmacy students and inspire them the way Dr. Smith has inspired me. I look forward to the challenges and rewards ahead of me as I continue in my pursuit to becoming a successful pharmacist.

Supplemental Application #1 for UCSF - Describe how you have explored Pharmacy and the Pharmaceutical Sciences to determine that this career path is for you.

Before college, my notion of a pharmacist's job was merely the dispensing of medications at retail pharmacies. My first true exposure to the field of pharmacy came during my sophomore year at a University XYZ's Pre-Pharmacy Society meeting. I was amazed at the numerous types of pharmacists and the specific disciplines that all fell under the broad term "pharmacy". My stereotype of pharmacists quickly dissipated and the diversity of the field fascinated me.

Since that first meeting, I began actively investigating a career in pharmacy through the Pre-Pharmacy Society (PPS). I felt fortunate to have a professional health organization on our campus that focused on pharmacy and jumped at the chance to attend each meeting. Since it was PPS that first introduced me to the field of pharmacy, I have always been passionate about the club. This passion motivated me to take the position of Vice President, where I could better serve the members and captivate them about pharmacy as my predecessors had done for me. I was also excited to work together with other pre-pharmacy students, who shared a common enthusiasm for pharmacy. We dedicated ourselves to informing our members about the profession through guest speakers, workshops, and volunteering events, and strived to improve our club by providing new informative resources, such as "Pharmacists of the Month" and "Drug of the Month." One of my favorite new resources our club offered was the opportunity to tour a variety of pharmacies.

One of the pharmacies we toured was a Compounding Pharmacy. During this visit, I've learned that certain patients have conditions that cannot be adequately treated by commercial products and therefore turn to compounding pharmacists to formulate a medication that will suit their personal needs. The exciting and challenging part of being a compounding pharmacist is dealing with unique and novel cases and using creative thinking to devise effective solutions. The attending compounding pharmacist shared with us one of his experiences where he dealt with a special patient who had olfactory problems. Due to a neurological defect, the patient interpreted the usual pleasant aromas as rotten and smelly odors. The compounding pharmacists were therefore asked to develop a medication that would be compatible with this unique patient's altered olfactory perceptions. I listened with great interest as the pharmacist described how he worked on each medication order as if he was solving a puzzle. The tour was a real eye opener and allowed me to see for myself the diversity of the career field that I had only heard about.

While I explored the differences among the many roles pharmacists can serve, I learned that they all share a common characteristic; they are all drug experts. Since I planned to become a drug expert in the future, I believed that it would be extremely beneficial for me to learn about medications ahead of time. Therefore, I decided to take a pharmacology class to strengthen my scientific background on medicine. It became one of my favorite classes in college! I was extremely excited when I recognized about 90% of the medications on a pharmacy shelf after finishing the course. I enjoyed the class tremendously as I studied common medications that are used to treat millions of Americans everyday, including my own friends and family! One of my plans for next quarter is to be the teacher's assistant for the same pharmacology class. This way, I will be able refresh the knowledge I had gained in preparing myself to be a pharmacist.

As I pursued pharmacy wholeheartedly, I took proactive steps to make sure the profession was right for me by exposing myself to different pharmacy settings. I found volunteering at the University XYZ Student Run Free Clinic to be one of the best opportunities I had to learn about pharmacy. I took the initiative to talk to the pharmacists and the pharmacy students and ask them questions each time I had a break between writing labels and recording information for the Patient Assistance Program. My experience at the clinic always gave me the chance to keep learning, whether it was reviewing the drugs I saw in pharmacology class or gaining new knowledge on an unfamiliar topic. I was excited to be able to learn from the pharmacy students by interacting closely with them, but I was even more thrilled to be able to learn along with them! On numerous occasions, the pharmacist came up with thought-provoking questions regarding a medication to test the pharmacy students' knowledge, such as why it is important not to take more than two puffs of Advair, and if patients were taking Advair and Albuterol concurrently, which medication should the patient take first. During those times, I listened intently with delight and learned along. What I love about volunteering at the clinic is that I always learned something new each time, whether it was specifics related to a drug's mechanism, how to deal with patients in different situations, or simply reading a medical code.

This past summer, I started working at Rite Aid as a Pharmacy clerk. Exposure to the hectic environment of a retail pharmacy has taught me the extreme importance of communicating well with the other Pharmacy staff and the patients, since one small miscommunication can lead to great confusions and unnecessary frustrations from both sides. I observed closely as my Pharmacy manager left notes in the medication bags to remind her and the other staff of what the previous situation was for that patient, in order to avoid any misunderstandings and mix-ups. Although I've only been working for a few months at Rite Aid Pharmacy, I have grown to love my work place. It is a very friendly environment where the pharmacy staff and patients know each other by name, and share a more personal, substantial relationship. Furthermore, because my pharmacy manager is good at her job, the pharmacy runs smoothly. I am constantly encouraged by the customers' expressions of gratitude for our store's ability to provide them with the proper medication in a short amount of time. Even though I have heard stories about how retail pharmacies can be a stressful place to work, I am currently seeing how great of a work place it can be when it is managed well.

I have finally come to know what I want in my lifelong career: a job that will give me immense joy and satisfaction through serving others by educating them on making the right medical decisions that will dramatically impact their health and improve their quality of life. From immersing myself in Pharmacy-related activities, I have found that career to be pharmacy.

Supplemental #2

1. Extracurricular, Leadership, Volunteer, Community Activities & Work Experience

Throughout high school and beginning of college, I was extremely nervous when I spoke in front of crowds. Whenever I gave a class presentation, I typically experienced three symptoms: flushed cheeks, a weak, squeaky voice, and shaky knees. During my sophomore year of college, I began to consider pharmacy as my future career goal. In order to be an effective pharmacist, I knew I would need to develop strong leadership and communication skills. To help strengthen these skills, I applied to teach an Organic Chemistry workshop. When I first started teaching, it was even harder than I had expected. I remember an intense feeling of horror sweeping over me as I stumbled my way through a poor explanation of "Retrosynthesis." Since then, to help ensure everything ran more smoothly, I spent hours before each workshop rehearsing my lesson plan in an empty study room. I planned out the ways I would use board space to present a new concept and came up with real life analogies relating to chemistry. I desired strongly for my teaching experience to not only help me grow stronger, but also have a great impact on my students' learning. Even though I was not required to attend the 8am class lecture, I saw it as an opportunity for me to review the course material and learn with the students. I attended every lecture and took the initiative to ask the professor any questions I had. Through teaching, I've not only gained a greater understanding of Organic Chemistry, but I've also acquired a strong confidence in my speaking abilities. From this experience, I learned how to engage students by asking questions that led them to think. Instead of assuming their level of understanding, I was able to evaluate their comprehension based off of their responses. As a future pharmacist, I will engage my patients to interact with me in the same way. When I encounter a patient that does not ask for the necessary counseling, I will make sure to ask them the appropriate questions that will lead them to respond to me. This way, I can ensure that they have a proper understanding of their medication.

2. Professional Acumen and Cultural Awareness

As I volunteered at the Free Clinic, a pharmacist pointed out the importance when writing prescription labels to use the word "daily" instead of "once" a day because "once" in Spanish means 11 and may mislead a Spanish speaking patient to take 11 tablets. In the following week, I informed the new volunteer about this problem so that she would also be aware of this serious issue. From this experience, I realized the necessity for a pharmacist to be well rounded and gain knowledge about different cultures since pharmacy is a profession that deals with all kinds of people. In a great anticipation to learn about various cultures, I obtained a job as a conversation leader for a class of International students. From observations, I realized that the students' behaviors in class were impacted by their cultural upbringings. The Asian students were often hesitant to answer the instructors' questions while the European students actively participated in class. This is because Asian culture tends to promote a passive learning style while Europeans were taught at a young age to express their opinions openly. To help the Asian students become more involved, I constantly encouraged them to speak up in class and advised them not to be afraid to speak, since it is the only way they can improve. Throughout time, I was excited to see an increase in their participation. From this experience, I've learned that awareness to a person's background will allow me to be more sensitive to that individual's needs. In the future, if I were to encounter a patient who has a hard time opening up, I would first take the patient to one side, and then ask if she has any questions she wants to ask me privately. In addition, I would clearly explain to her that the information she is sharing is completely confidential so that she feels comfortable to disclose any personal information.

3. Personal Perspective

This past summer, I went to El Salvador to volunteer at a health clinic. While shadowing the physician there, I noticed something subtle that he did that touched an emotional chord within me. Before checking the patient's vitals, he went to wash his hands. The strange thing was, he had washed his hands just moments prior to walking into the room. At that moment, I realized that he had purposely washed his hands again purely to comfort the patient. I was touched by the strong sensitivity and consideration he demonstrated toward his patients and inspired by his deep understanding of their needs.

During this same summer, while working at Rite Aid Pharmacy, I came upon a patient who was purchasing her medication along with a bottle of ice cold coca cola and a birthday card. While bagging her items, I placed the coca cola along with her medication in one bag, and took out a second bag for her birthday card. The patient looked at me curiously and asked, "Why did you use two bags?" I answered, "Oh, I didn't want the water on the outside of your drink to get your card wet." The patient's face displayed her pleasant surprise as she smiled and thanked me for my thoughtfulness.

Reflecting upon both experiences, I realize that it is a human compassion that the physician and I share in common that heightens our sensitivity toward others. I have come to understood that when interacting with people, small, thoughtful gestures can strongly impact the way the other person feels. As a future health professional who will deal with sensitive medical issues, my acuteness and sensitivity toward people's feelings will help my interactions with patients. I will go out of my way to make my patients feel comfortable. As a result, I will be able to establish open and trusting relationships which will allow me to better care for them.

4. Other Information (Optional)

As I pursued pharmacy wholeheartedly, I took proactive steps to make sure the profession was right for me. At the University XYZ Free Clinic, I took the initiative to talk to the pharmacists and the pharmacy students each time I had a break between writing labels and recording information for the Patient Assistance Program. I was excited to be able to learn from the pharmacy students by interacting closely with them, but I was even more thrilled to be able to learn along with them! On numerous occasions, the pharmacist came up with thought-provoking questions regarding a medication to test the pharmacy students' knowledge, such as why it is important not to take more than two puffs of Advair, and if patients were taking Advair and Albuterol concurrently, which medication should the patient take first. During those times, I listened intently with delight and learned along. What I love about volunteering at the clinic is that I always learned something new each time, whether it was specifics related to a drug's mechanism, how to deal with patients in different situations, or simply reading a medical code. This past summer, I started working at Rite Aid as a Pharmacy clerk. Exposure to the hectic environment of a retail pharmacy has taught me the extreme importance of communicating well with the other Pharmacy staff and the patients, since one small miscommunication can lead to great confusions and unnecessary frustrations from both sides. I observed closely as my Pharmacy manager left notes in the medication bags to remind her and the other staff of what the previous situation was for that patient, in order to avoid any misunderstandings. Although I've only been working for a few months at Rite Aid Pharmacy, I have grown to love my work place. It is a very friendly environment where the pharmacy staff and patients know each other by name, and share a more personal, substantial relationship. Furthermore, because my pharmacy manager is good at her job, the pharmacy runs smoothly.

I am constantly encouraged by the customers' expressions of gratitude for our store's ability to provide them with the proper medication in a short amount of time. Even though I have heard stories about how retail pharmacies can be a stressful place to work, I am currently seeing how great of a work place it can be when it is managed well. Immersing myself in these pharmacy-related activities has further intensified my passion toward this career path.

5. Candidate's Statement

While my potential classmates at UCSF and I will share similar accomplishments with regards to our pursuits in academia and research, I believe that my compassion and strong character serve as qualities that distinguish me as a viable candidate for acceptance.

When I first started working for University XYZ Extension Program as a conversation leader this summer, I came across a Korean student named Sarah. She had arrived in the United States only a month earlier, so her limited English-language skills featured a heavy Korean accent and considerable problems with comprehension. When Sarah approached me after class one day to ask if I could dedicate some time every week to tutoring her in English, I was hesitant to commit myself to another obligation in an already busy schedule. At that time, besides my work as a conversation leader, I was volunteering in a research lab at a clinic downtown, working as a Pharmacy clerk at Rite Aide, had the start of my summer classes looming, and was also signed up for the Pharmacy technician exam just a month later. I considered saying no with my plate as full as it was, but somehow, I couldn't turn her down. I had seen the drive with which she strove to overcome her limitation through the significant effort she invested in class. I observed and strongly related to her determination for self-improvement, and took it as a challenge to myself to make sure that her labor did not end up in vain. With my schedule ever-present in the back of my mind, I agreed to tutor her an hour after each of our class.

In our first session, Sarah and I took the time to get to know each other. Throughout our conversation, I corrected sentence structure and grammar errors. I also had a present prepared for her. I recalled that she had mentioned a specific desire to improve her vocabulary, so I decided to give her a notebook for her to use to write any word she encounters in her daily activities that she hopes to learn. I knew she would appreciate the notebook, and I couldn't wait to give it to her. The moment I showed her the present, her whole face lit up! It felt so great to see that a small notebook had made her so happy. For the rest of that day, I couldn't stop smiling.

I have worked hard towards bettering myself through the productive application of my time and efforts, but Sarah reminded me the importance of taking time to help my peers. As a potential student in UCSF's Pharmacy School, I will use the valuable education I will gain for more than my own personal betterment and gain, but as a resource for helping others.

Supplemental #3 for WesternU

1. What attracts you to a career in pharmacy? Is there an area of practice that is of particular interest to you?

Through a process of exploration and self reflection in college, I have finally come to know what I want in my lifelong career: a job that will give me immense joy and satisfaction through serving others and making an impact on their lives. From immersing myself in Pharmacy-related activities, I have found that career to be pharmacy. The major attraction of pharmacy for me is that it is a job where I get the chance to interact closely with people daily. As a pharmacist, I will cherish the strong relationships I will have with other health professionals, fellow pharmacists, and the patients I will be serving. Furthermore, I have been amazed by the extraordinary diversity of the field ever since the first time I was introduced to pharmacy at a Pre-Pharmacy Society meeting. From talking to different pharmacists, I have learned that a Pharm D degree is a door-opener and a stepping stone to many new, exciting opportunities. From volunteering at the University XYZ Free Clinic, a clinic that is dedicated to serving the local homeless community, I have also come to see the dramatic differences pharmacists make in the lives of those who are less fortunate. This experience has led me to discover my interest in working at community pharmacies.

2. Explain what you have done to prepare yourself as a future pharmacist.

To find out if Pharmacy is right for me, I volunteered at different pharmacy settings. At the University XYZ Free Clinic, I took initiative to talk to the pharmacists and pharmacy students whenever I had a break between writing labels. While the pharmacist asked thought-provoking questions to test the Pharmacy students' knowledge, I listened intently with delight and learned along. Furthermore, it was exciting whenever I recognized a drug at the clinic from Pharmacology class. If I had forgotten its use, I made sure to ask and find out. What I love about volunteering at the clinic is that I always learned something new each time I went, whether it was related to a drug's mechanism, dealing with patients, or simply reading a medical code. I took notes on everything, because I knew these notes will benefit me greatly when I enter Pharmacy School. Exposure to Pharmacy also made me realize the importance of strong leadership and communication skills. To strengthen these skills, I undertook various leadership and teaching positions. Recently, I have just started working at Rite Aid as a Pharmacy clerk. I am excited for my new learning experience that will prepare me even further for a successful career in Pharmacy!

3. If you are a re-applicant, explain what you have done in the past year to enhance your application.

I am a new applicant.

4. Aside from becoming a pharmacist, what other professional and personal goals do you have? How do you plan to achieve them?

One of my professional goals is to improve people's health through increasing the awareness of health. I've learned that the U.S. health care system focuses mainly on the diagnosis and treatment of diseases, and neglects the importance of health promotion. When I enter Pharmacy School, I plan to achieve this goal through volunteering at different health clinics and becoming involved in a variety of organizations that works to educate the public on how to be healthy. I also plan to teach health classes on topics such as nutrition and hygiene at different universities. I think it is extremely important to take a preventive perspective when it comes to dealing with diseases. One of my personals goals is to mentor children and students in the future and help them make better decisions that will impact their lives. This coming, new year, I plan to participate in mentoring programs such as "Big Brothers Big Sisters" and "University XYZ San

Diego Bright Families Project." From my own experience as a mentee, I have come to realize the huge differences a great mentor can make in a person's life.

5. Identify one social problem in the United States that is of concern to you. What do you believe are some possible solutions?

One of the biggest social problems in U.S. that I am concerned about is that millions of Americans do not have health insurance, and are not able to afford health care. After watching the film, "Sicko," by Michael Moore, I learned more about the inside workings of Health Insurance Companies, and began to wonder why a powerful nation like America have such a horrible health system. I believe that a possible solution to this problem is Universal Healthcare, which can be maintained through increasing taxes. Furthermore, I believe that the U.S. needs to increase the funding for public health and invest more money into prevention programs for different type of diseases. Education and advertising campaigns should be used to make people more aware of what's causing common health problems, and more money should be spent on Public health education.

6. Name an individual whom you admire greatly. Why?

An individual I admire greatly is my mentor, Dr. Smith. Dr. Smith showed me how a great pharmacist is someone who is a great teacher and loves to educate others through sharing his own knowledge and wisdom. Even after he had retired, he continued to volunteer at community pharmacies, and offered his time to mentor 13 different mentees. He truly enjoys teaching and continued teaching health classes in San Diego State College and National University. I had the opportunity to attend one of Dr. Smith's classes through his generous invitation. In a matter of 4 hours, I had learned a great deal about pharmaceutical products. When Dr. Smith taught in class, it didn't seem like he was lecturing to the students. He simply talked to them like a friend, and shared with them his own experiences. It was such an effective way of teaching! Whenever I shared my goals with Dr. Smith, he offered me great encouragement and gave me very personal and helpful advice. I took all of his counsel to heart because I knew he is a wise man who genuinely cares for my success. I have come to know Dr. Smith as someone who always did more than what his job required and really cares about the people he is affecting. I aspire to be a caring pharmacist just like him!

7. What are your strongest and weakest personal characteristics? How have these strength(s) and weakness(s) helped or hindered you in the achievement of your goals?

My greatest strength is that I am able to focus on what's really important to me and work very hard at it. When I first came to college, I felt that I lacked strong leadership skills. Therefore, I strived to improve by welcoming new experiences. I became very involved in the Pre-Pharmacy Society and attended every event that was offered. I went on to become the Co-Vice president of the club. I faced a tough challenge when I first started teaching an Organic Chemistry workshop. To make sure everything ran smoothly, I spent hours before each workshop rehearsing my lesson plan in an empty study room. One of my weaknesses used to be that I was very nervous whenever I spoke in front of a crowd. I am proud to say that I have overcome that weakness. I challenged myself to stand in front of 30 students and teach them, when it was difficult for me to just speak in front of a small group of people. I threw myself into unfamiliar situations, and stepped out of my comfort zone. As a result, I grew and changed dramatically in college. Another one of my weakness is that I worry too much, even when I am doing well. This led to creating unnecessary stress for myself. But I have come to realize that this weakness can be seen as one of my strengths. The reason I worry is because I care. When I care tremendously about something such as getting into pharmacy school, I worry a lot about it. And because I worry, I work even harder to make sure I accomplish my goals.

8. Have you worked during the school year? If so, how many hours per week? If admitted, do you plan or need to work while attending the School of Pharmacy? If so, how many hours per week?

During the school year, I worked at many different types of jobs. I worked about 10 hours a week as a workshop leader in a tutorial center. I later switched from being a workshop leader to being a teacher's assistant, where I also worked about 10 hours a week. At the same time, I was also working about 12 hours as week at a Pharmaceutical Company. Currently, I am working about 10 hours a week as a teacher's assistant and about 12 hours a week at Rite Aid as a Pharmacy clerk. It was challenging at first balancing both school and work. The only reason I was able to adjust to my busy schedule was because I planned everything out. I did not try to do everything at once. Instead, I slowly added a new activity after I have already adjusted to my previous new job. As I dedicated myself to my jobs, I understood that school is still the top priority on my list. In order to maintain excellent academic performance while I was working, I made sure to take only certain amount of units per quarter so that I would be able to balance school, work, and other activities. I understood my limits and knew myself very well in how much I can handle. From juggling different jobs while balancing school, I have been trained to manage my time wisely and have grown tremendously from all of my varied work experiences.

If admitted, I do plan to work while attending school. I believe the specific hands on experience and the insightful knowledge you gain from a work place is something you cannot get from a classroom. I plan to work at least 10 hours a week, but not too much that it jeopardizes my studying. I greatly value the exceptional learning experience that I get from work.

However, I will never let work get in the way of my studying. I will adjust my working hours according to my course load and my abilities.

9. Describe your participation in extra-curricular activities (campus and/or community) - that you feel may enhance your application. Include all offices and other leadership positions held. If you have not participated, indicate why.

I have been teaching Organic Chemistry for two years and have truly enjoyed the experience. When I first started teaching an Organic Chemistry workshop, I was determined to make an impact on my students' learning. Even though I was not required to attend the 8am class lecture, I saw it as an opportunity for me to review the course material and learn with the students. I attended every lecture and took the initiative to ask the professor any questions I had. As a result, my own understanding of the course material improved greatly and I was able to explain the concepts very well to my students. One of the characteristics that will help me succeed in a career in pharmacy is my great desire and willingness to learn. Furthermore, I have been involved in the Pre-Pharmacy Society (PPS) for three years. I am extremely passionate about PPS because it was the organization that introduced me to pharmacy. From my experiences as a public relations officer and co-vice president, I have learned how to handle my responsibilities and allow others to depend on me. I also learned how to work together with people that have very different personalities. Furthermore, I've learned that one of the key factors to being a strong communicator is to have confidence in yourself. From initiating conversations with the members, leading discussions in the officer meetings, and standing in front of a large group of people sharing my own experiences, I have gained great confidence in my abilities to communicate. Through my involvement, I've also established many lasting friendships. From these experiences, I have had the opportunity to care for others and have grown to become more understanding and patient.

10. Describe some of your non-academic interests (e.g., recreational or athletic activities, hobbies, club participation etc.)

In high school, I had always loved playing sports in physical education class, but I never had the time or the skills to play on a professional school team. Therefore, when I became involved in the Pre-Pharmacy Society, I suggested the idea of starting our own Intramural Sports team. I believed that having our own sports team would allow the members in our organization to get to know each other better and create a sense of teamwork among our club. After sharing my idea with the other officers, they agreed that it would make our club more social and fun. In Fall Quarter of 2007, Team PPS was born! The Co-president and I coordinated the Dodge ball team together in Fall Quarter, and it turned out so successful that we decided to continue with a Co-Ed Basketball team in winter quarter and finish with a Co-Ed volleyball team in spring quarter. Because we had signed up for the Beginner's league, there wasn't a ton of pressure for us to win, and the games were all about having fun! We bonded through our weekly team practices and games. At the end the year, I've made many strong friendships with the other team members. The experience I had playing for Team PPS became one of the most memorable experiences in my last year of college.

11. Have you had any academic difficulties that may appear on your transcripts that you would like to explain?

When I first entered college, it was difficult for me to transition to a new place that was very far away from home. The first quarter was especially challenging for me to adjust to, which showed in my academic performance. However, I continued to strive to improve myself. I came into college not knowing what I wanted for my future career. As I explored different career options in sophomore year, I was introduced to pharmacy in a Pre-Pharmacy Society meeting, and became immediately attracted to the profession. In the spring quarter of my sophomore year, I made a solid decision to pursue pharmacy. Since then, I have no hesitation to say that I have worked my hardest to achieve academic excellence and I am proud to see that it shows on my academic record. The pursuit of pharmacy was the unwavering goal that strongly motivated me to achieve my best.

12. Please use space below to make any additional personal comments that you think will strengthen your application.

A personal quality that has led me to pharmacy is my strong compassion to help others. When I first started working as a conversation leader this summer, I met an International student from Korea named Sarah. Although she spoke with limited English, she always tried very hard to participate in class. I observed her determination to improve and strongly related to her perseverance to overcome challenges. After class one day, Sarah approached me privately and asked if I could spend some time every week to tutor her in English. I was struggling with the idea because of my extremely busy schedule. I was volunteering at a research lab and at the University XYZ Downtown clinic. I was also working as a conversation leader. Furthermore, I was studying for the Pharmacy Technician Exam that I was about to take a month later. On top of that, I was going to start my summer class soon and begin working at Rite Aid as a Pharmacy clerk. I was about to say no, but when I saw the desperate look Sarah gave me, somehow, I just couldn't say no to her. I smiled and said, "Sure, we'll work something out." I knew in my heart that it would be worth it to take some time out to help her. Just from our first meeting, Sarah and I got to know each other well. Throughout our conversation, I corrected her sentence structure and grammar errors. I also had a present prepared for her. It was a notebook for her to take notes on all the new vocabulary that she will learn. I knew she would love the notebook, and I couldn't wait to give it to her. The moment I showed it to her, her whole face lit up! It felt so great to see that a small notebook had made her so happy. For the rest of that day, I couldn't stop smiling. As a pharmacist, I look forward to impacting the lives of my patients the way I had impacted Sarah's life.

Supplemental #4 for UOP

From talking directly to the Pacific Pharmacy students, I have learned tremendously about the school and have discovered that it is a strong match to what I am looking for in a pharmacy school.

The major attraction of University of Pacific for me is that it strongly values and provides a student-centered learning environment. I have heard wonderful stories about caring faculties and staffs who take into account the students' comments and concerns. I learned that professors at Pacific really want students to succeed, and would go as far as to change the point breakdown in the class to prevent any student from failing. I was pleasantly surprised to hear that one of the professors even took the measures of changing a whole textbook because students complained about it.

What also showed me that the school is extremely focused on student centered learning is that they provide many benefits for the students. I've learned that at the beginning of the year, each student is leased a tablet computer to help with note taking. I also really like the fact that each class provides a class liaison that meets with the professor weekly or biweekly to relay to the professors the students' concerns. The fact that UOP organizes all these fantastic benefits for the students showed me that the school really attends to the students needs.

Another captivating quality about UOP is that it is a small community where everyone gets to know each other very well. After attending such a large school such as University XYZ, I would love to change to a school with a smaller campus. The small class size would allow me to get the personal attention from the professors that I never got in University XYZ and give me the chance to interact closely with my classmates. Furthermore, I learned that UOP provides a cooperative working atmosphere where everyone helps each other out through sharing information and old notes. I look forward to building long lasting friendships with my classmates through the close interactions. The world of pharmacy is so small that you're bound to run into someone you know from pharmacy school at your future workplace. It would be great for me to start building strong relationships with my Pharmacy school classmates who will most likely be my future colleagues.

A strong focus on student activities is also what draws me to UOP. I am impressed by the abundance and the variety of student organizations that are offered on the campus, which gives me the confidence that I will be able to find an organization that suits my interests. I am also extremely interested in the numerous leadership positions that are offered by the school, such as co-chair for Operation Diabetes, Operation Immunization, and American Heart Association, which will help me further develop and strengthen my leadership skills. I learned that as a pharmacy student intern at UOP, I will get the opportunity to organize and participate in a variety of public health screenings that include immunizations, measuring blood pressure, cholesterol levels, and blood glucose levels. From doing online research, I've come to find that these public health screenings make a huge impact on the Stockton community, where the majority of the populations are low income families who have Medi-cal for their healthcare financial support. I would be thrilled to go to UOP and get the chance to make an impact on people who really need the help.

Another characteristic of UOP that strongly appeals to me is their focus on issues of diversity and equality. From studying the UOP website, I have learned about the multiple programs that are designed to promote and emphasize the importance of cultural diversity and awareness, such as the Multicultural Affairs and the Gender studies program. I personally believe very strongly in the importance of cultural diversity in the community and the need for everyone to be open to people with different backgrounds. Examining the statistics of the demographics of UOP and talking to the Pacific pharmacy students has shown me that UOP has a diverse student body, a wide range of faculty and staff, and a strong commitment to building a diverse campus community.

Other than all the terrific traits mentioned above, another alluring quality about UOP is its unique Accelerated 3 year Pharm D program. After making some meticulous calculations, I have discovered that attending UOP would save me the most money in comparison to attending the other pharmacy schools, since I would be able to start working as a full time pharmacist in my fourth year. Coming from a low income family, financial problems are always one of my biggest concerns. Because I already took up a large amount of loans for my undergraduate study in University XYZ, it is in my best interest to start working early and begin paying off the huge burden of loans on my shoulders. In addition, other UOP students have informed me about the cheap, but highest ranked affordable housing that's available in Stockton. After planning out my finances in pharmacy school, I have no doubts that I would save a huge amount of money living in Stockton compared to living in other expensive areas such as San Diego and San Francisco. Considering the financial aspect, UOP is definitely the school that most corresponds to my needs.

Furthermore, the location of UOP also appeals to my interest since it is very close to home. All of my family lives in Northern California in the bay area, and going to UOP would give me the chance to visit them often. Because I went to University XYZ for my undergraduate study, I was always far away from home. I was sad that I wasn't able to visit my family other than the occasional summer and winter breaks. Becoming a UOP pharmacy student would allow me to move back to Northern California and be closer to my family.

After learning about the specific features that UOP offered, I have no reservations when I say that UOP is the right school for me. I am confident that the University of Pacific will fully prepare me for a lifelong success in the Pharmacy profession

Candidate #2

GPA 3.4, Accepted into WesternU, Northstate

PharmCAS Personal Statement

I remember holding packets of Chinese medicine herbs and staring blankly at the lady operating the pharmacy. "Next!" she roared in Chinese at the next customer. As a foreigner with a four-day 102F fever in rural China, I discovered that "pharmacist" in the Western sense does not exist in China. It was here that I realized the importance of the pharmacist's role in advising patients, physicians and other health practitioners, on dosage, selection, side effects and interactions of medication.

I have volunteered at the University QRS Student Health Center Pharmacy and observed on-site patient counseling. I found that a unique part about being a pharmacist is interacting with people of different cultures, backgrounds, and disabilities while overcoming language barriers. Having experienced feelings of being lonely and lost in my study abroad trip in China, I felt relieved when I became friends with a native student in China, as she was able to guide and help me through difficult situations.

Thus, as a Conversation Leader at University QRS extension ELI (English Language Institute), I was able to do the same for international students. Essentially a teacher's assistant for ELI's Conversation classes, I lead small group discussions with students from at least five different countries. I found immense joy in conversing with people of different cultures. As a Conversation Leader, I mastered techniques to break down language and social barriers with my students, to the extent that my students would tell me about their personal troubles. As a future pharmacist, I am able to break down disability, language, and cultural barriers, and earn the trust of a patient in order to clearly educate the patient on the side effects, treatment duration and application frequency of the medication.

Out of the numerous pharmacists I interviewed, oncology pharmacist Dr. Mary Davis advice stands out. Mary explained that a pharmacist is the last line of defense on the medical team, providing the final check on the medication before it is given to the patient. She strongly emphasized that attention to details is imperative. For example, a pharmacist in her hospital gave a patient ten times the dosage needed for chemotherapy treatment, a nearly fatal mistake. From this, I learned that a pharmacist can significantly impact the lives of a patient and those around them.

In college, I worked on an independent research project at University QRS's medical research lab for Professor Smith. My responsibility was to use techniques of cell culture, Western blotting, and protein quantification to identify the presence of Chromogrannin A, a parathyroid secretory protein that is a tumor marker for prostate cancer cells. I learned that research requires analytical and problem solving skills, because often times I obtained unexpected results and had to backtrack each step of the research process to identify the error. Slightly touching the pipette on the non-sterile edge of the reagent bottle could potentially contaminate the cell media, which destroy months of hard work and research. In this lab, I excelled in the skills of problem solving and paying meticulously attention to details. As a future pharmacist, I am prepared to take on the difficult and challenging situations in the pharmacy as my actions will make a direct difference to each patient.

In 2007, I volunteered at the Hillcrest branch for University QRS Medical Hospital in the Ambulatory Care Outpatient Pharmacy where most of the patients were from the comprehensive cancer center. Emotional and depressed patients frequented the pharmacy after being diagnosed with malignant cancer or undergoing chemotherapy. Dr. Lisa Johnson, the head pharmacist showed great compassion and care towards each patient as she spends one on one time educating and at the same time comforting them about their medical condition. I learned that pharmacists should not only dispense and consult with patients, but also follow up and assure that patients are well taken care of to the end of the treatment. I felt inspired and greatly moved by her compassion to relieve their suffering and pain not only through medicine, but through understanding and honesty. Seeing how Lisa could directly comfort and personally affect other human beings also solidified my decision that pharmacy is the right path for me. I want to be a pharmacist like her, dedicating my life to serving others.

Candidate #3

PharmCAS Personal Statement for International Students applying to 3-year pharmD program.

'Giant oaks owe their strength to their roots'. In my case it has been the foundation of my education which is deeply penetrated in the principles of discipline, knowledge and truth. It is my pleasure to be associated with a field that strives to serve humanity and cherish the wonderful gift of life.

Presently, I am doing pre-requisites for the Pharm.D program at Idaho State University. I have also completed four year Bachelor's degree in Pharmacy from Karnataka Lingayat Education (K.L.E) Society College of Pharmacy, Karnataka, India; affiliated to Rajiv Gandhi University of Health Science, Bangalore. The National Board of accreditation AICTE New Delhi has awarded grade 'A' to the institution for period of last 5 years. I have completed my schooling (high school) from Seventh Day Adventist, India; entirely in English medium. The school is affiliated to Indian School Certificate Examination Board New Delhi.

Although I entered college without a clear research direction, the Pharmacy curriculum at K.L.E. Society's College of Pharmacy, Belgaum instigated my interest in the field of Pharmacy. The undergraduate curriculum provided me thorough grounding in core subjects like Pharmacology, Pharmaceutical Chemistry (Medicinal Chemistry), Pharmaceutical Technology, Pharmaceutical Analysis, Industrial Pharmacognosy, Pharmaceutical Management and Pharmaceutical Microbiology etc. Final year proved to be most defining phase due to the fact that it was this period that invoked the dormant interest in me related to Pharmacology, Pharmaceutical Chemistry and Pharmaceutical technology.

In my final year one of my professors in Medicinal Chemistry assigned me a project on the topic 'URINARY TRACT ANTI-INFECTIVES'. In doing this project I came across many details about Urinary Tract Infection (UTI) i.e. how it is caused, what are its preventive measures, what type of different medicines are used for its treatment, etc. After doing this project my interest rose in studying how medicines are made, what type of equipments are used, etc. These questions were answered when I did my industrial training. An industrial training at a well-known company Lincoln Pharmaceuticals Ltd. in Ahmedabad (India) during my 3rd year was something that I enjoyed most. The two-months training introduced me to the manufacturing processes of various dosage forms and provided me with an exposure to the manufacturing industry and different departments thereof like research and development, quality control laboratory and quality assurance department.

Besides being academically strong, I have an inclination towards sports and have actively taken part in almost all sportive activities in school and college. I have also secured certificates in sports activity like Cricket, Tennis.

I am working as a Certified Pharmacy Technician at Walgreens Rx since Feb '07. My duties include receiving written prescriptions or requests for prescription refills from patients. Also, I'm responsible for receiving prescriptions sent electronically from the doctor's office. I prepare the prescription, retrieve, count, pour, weigh, measure, and sometimes help mix the medication. I also have to establish and maintain patient profiles and prepare insurance claim forms. When I see the pharmacist assisting and counseling the patient, I realize the job, though exacting, has a greater satisfaction to help mankind directly. Also, a growing awareness of and experimentation with new ways to deliver medical care that is more cost-effective, efficient, and patient-centered has allowed pharmacists to begin to redefine themselves as deliverers of care rather than counters of pills. With the explosion in biomedical science knowledge, pharmacists can choose to "ride the wave" from a clinical-care perspective too.

In today's competitive scenario I feel that an industry or a professional needs constant research and technical advancement. Also, understanding various aspects of pharmacy laws to practice pharmacy under different types of settings, like clinical, hospital, community and nuclear to name a few, is challenging. Hence, if I have to survive and progress in future, it is imperative for me to be equipped with the latest advancement in the field of Pharmacy. In spite of being a licensed pharmacist in India, I am determined to obtain a license in United States so I can learn the different aspects of pharmacy laws in different countries. I feel the Pharm D program at your esteemed university is the best way I can satisfy my entrepreneurial interest (in long terms) and gain access to the cutting edge competition in the global scale prospective and also help patients directly.

I have realized that education is a progressive discovery of one's own ignorance. I envisage myself as a determined person and I want to create new structure of medicine, which may help in future to the whole world. With high education, focused goals and existing talents, I am confident to excel in meeting my objectives and offer substantial contribution to the field of Health care. I am aware that the College of Pharmacy at your prestigious University expects very high standards from its students. On my part, I can assure you of sincerity and hard work. I am confident that my enthusiasm will enable me to meet your expectations.

Candidate #4

GPA 3.5, Accepted into WesternU, MCPHS at Worcester

PharmCAS Personal Statement

My decision to pursue a career in pharmacy was made based on my interests in the applications of science, my passion for lifelong learning, and the potential for the pharmacy profession to alleviate human pain and suffering caused by illnesses. At the tender age of six, I remember choosing school over my parents' eager invitation of an oversea trip because I did not want to miss the thrill of opening a new chapter in class. As soon as I learned how to read, I found myself fascinated by new scientific discoveries, especially those related to medicines that promised an end to certain diseases. I even dreamed of becoming a scientist who made "magical pills" to save the world. That was a childish dream, but it propelled me to work hard in the hope that I would one day make headlines.

When I was one of three Cambodians who won the scholarship to Singapore, I felt nothing would stop me from realizing my dream. I soon discovered that my academic journey was replete with challenges, which stemmed mainly from my need to overcome the English language barrier. I must admit that there were moments when I was on the verge of giving up. However, I kept reminding myself that it took power to persevere at times when people would understand if I were to fall apart. With great determination, I managed to blossom in the Singapore environment, acquiring solid knowledge in science which enabled me to continue my education in the United States.

I first heard of PharmD when I moved to California in 2005 to begin my college education. I researched the program and was excited to learn about its potential to help sick people get well and to serve the community through frequent interactions with patients. Growing up in a war-torn, third world nation, where health care access is limited and infectious diseases are rampant, I was motivated to search for a solution that emphasizes cost-effective treatments and accessibility, which is relevant to pharmacy. Although I was clearly attracted to pharmacy, I did not commit myself to it until having first explored other fields of interest through volunteering at a local hospital, participating in health-related clubs, and working as a salesperson which allowed me to interact with customers and solidify my desire to work in a field where I can interact and help people.

As I cared for the patients in the cardiothoracic center and the emergency floor at Huntington hospital, the images of people who could not afford medical care relentlessly flashed through my mind. I thought of my parents who, like most other Cambodians, always avoided hospital visits for fear of discovering debilitating illnesses/diseases which would imply financial ruin to the whole family. I thought of the homeless people I saw throughout my childhood whose lives could have been improved or saved with a few medications. I thought of how grateful I was for the pharmacist who spotted the abnormality of my skin color and thus helped in the diagnosis and treatment of my Hepatitis A when I was a child. These thoughts and the fact that pharmacists are easily reached by the general public attract me even more to pharmacy.

Through my participation in health-related clubs, I confirmed my interest in pharmacy. Listening to and interacting with different types of pharmacists and pharmacy students who came to share their pharmacy experiences with Caduceus club and Pre-pharmacy Society, I learned that pharmacists' responsibilities go beyond the technical function of filling a prescription; patient-oriented care and the outcome of service are usually, if not always, the main focus. The diversity and the dynamics of pharmacy means that one needs to always keep up with the constantly changing health care environment like the emergence of new infectious diseases and new ways of handling them. That excites me. That is exactly what I would like to do regularly and as a professional pharmacist.

My decision to become a pharmacist was made after exploring many professions through volunteering in hospital and working in sales as well as consolidating my interests in science, my love for lifelong learning, and the potential of pharmacy in healing others. I am by no means an extraordinary individual with any special talents. However, I am very determined and I always persevere in the face of every obstacle. The spirit of never giving up has always been, and will always be, with me as I follow my heart and pursue my dream to become a pharmacist.

Supplementary Application Essays

Personality can tell a great deal about a person, be it the behavior, the quality of life, or even one's future. It is probably the most crucial determinant of one's destiny. Although there are many things that I want people to know about me, I will illustrate only three characteristics of mine which, I hope, will give you a clearer picture of me.

Being helpful is one of my traits. I enjoy helping others ranging from my family to strangers. When my mother was bedridden with pneumonia, I purchased the groceries for the household, at the tender age of ten. Whenever my sister did the cooking, I would lend her a helping hand, like her personal sous-chef. I looked after my parents' store during my free time. As a Subject Representative, I went beyond the call of duty by printing all the notes for my classmates. When examinations were approaching, I devoted some time to tutoring my friends inside and outside the classroom. I helped educate Thai villagers in Chiang Mai on organic farming during my school break. Throughout my educational journey in Cambodia, Singapore, and the United States, I often took time off to listen and help friends who needed me. In retrospect, I realize that these memories have added meanings to my life because they give me a sense of true happiness and fulfillment.

Cheerfulness has brought me friends, joys and other blessings. I love seeing other people happy, because it simply makes me happy too. Watching comedy and sharing humor with the others fill my life and theirs with laughter. While many students complained about the stressful education in Singapore, I viewed studying there as a blessing. It not only provided a challenging education for me to blossom in, but also taught me the importance of living in harmony with other cultures in a multi-ethnic society. In response to the multitude of conflicts populating our world, I stand firm to my belief that with respect and tolerance, peace is attainable. Life is not a bed of roses, but it needs not be a path of thorns.

Treating others as we would like to be treated is important. I believe if everyone could do this, conflict would be a word consigned in history. Respecting my elders and peers comes naturally to me. Even when others at times offended me, I reminded myself that there was a reason behind their actions. Only once one understands another's motives will one be able to understand his/her behaviors. The milieu in which one develops and the upbringing of that person are critical in determining an individual's personality. Understanding these make me tolerant towards others. Given sufficient and rational explanation of what is right and wrong, one's mindset can be changed. However, I will not seek to mold anyone in my image, as it is crucial to respect the diversity of peoples' views. Respecting people is a basic tenet of my life.

Living my life and viewing the world as described above have served to make me who I am today. I would not claim that my personalities are the most desirable attributes out there, nor would I say that they would bring me fame and fortune. However, I believe that they will help me not only in terms of understanding how humans are being conditioned to behave the ways they do but also in forgiving those who have caused harms to others and the society as a result of human flaws. These are the personalities that I hope would distinguish me from other applicants. These are the personalities that I will bring with me to (ABC University). These are the personalities that I will bring to my pharmacy profession.

Master the Interview

You will receive an interview invitation if your application passes the scrutiny of the school's admission officer. If you do not receive an interview invitation, review your pharmacy admission portfolio to identify areas that need improvement. Whether it's your personal statement, your grades, your PCAT score, etc., find out what's dragging you down and level it up.

For those of you who did get an interview invite, congratulations! The battle is not over yet, but the tides are turning in your favor. The school has expressed an interest in accepting you. All that's left for you to do is to ace the interview.

Why is it so important that you master your interview?

The interview can make or break your chances of getting into a school. If you are one of those students who are borderline for being accepted, doing well at your interview may give you a boost. In a casual conversation with a dean of admissions, we found out that there were multiple occasions on which a student interviewed with an average GPA but did so well during the interview that the interviewer became an advocate for their admission. Conversely, if you are a strong candidate (i.e. with a great personal statement and high GPA/high PCAT score) but you botch your interview, you may lose your chances of being accepted. Make no mistake, the interview is a crucial part of your admissions process and both strategy and practice are going to be critical to your success.

As the man on the hundred-dollar bill once said, "By **failing to prepare**, you are **preparing to fail.**" Like Benjamin Franklin, we believe that proper preparation is essential and should be developed accordingly, not just for your interview but for your pharmacy career in general.

How to Answer Unexpected Questions

This section teaches you how to formulate your answers in the best way possible. Remember, your interviewers can ask you anything. We are all afraid of the nightmare scenario where the interviewers ask you a curve-ball question leaving you absolutely flabbergasted. You sit there, mouth agape with eyes wide open in panic. You eventually give an incoherent, obviously made-up answer. Practice the following methods to avoid finding yourself in a similar situation.

Step 1: Pick three characteristics you want to sell about yourself. These are characteristics that would make you a good pharmacist. We have provided several characteristics below that pharmacy schools highly value.

Characteristics

1. Meticulous/attentive to details
2. Passion for helping others
3. Interpersonal skills – being a people person
4. Love of science and lifelong learning
5. Leadership skills
6. Time management skills

Step 2: For each of the three characteristics you picked, come up with two stories that demonstrate that specific characteristic. Remember, pick genuine and true stories! This is the reason why it is so important to volunteer or work in a pharmacy as you will be able to draw upon real-life experiences. An applicant we worked with took notes of inspirational moments throughout her volunteer and work experiences a year *before* she interviewed then put them to use during her interview.

Set aside a notepad or a Word document just for your pharmacy experiences and jot down anything you saw, learned or experienced that inspired you. You can then use these notes for your ideas at your interview or on your personal statement. If you have two stories for each of the three characteristics that you picked, you have six compelling stories in your interview bank. You can even combine your themes in one story or have your stories overlap between two questions. When you come up with your answer, try to tie your story in with *why* you want to go to pharmacy school or *how* you can use your acquired skills to better help your patients' lives as a pharmacist.

Example story showing "passion for helping others"

When I was volunteering at the pharmacy clinic, there was a patient who was very anxious about taking her medication for hyperthyroidism. The patient had no medical issues all her life and this was her first time having a major medical issue where she would have to take daily medication. She was extremely distressed. My pharmacist, Dr. Robinson, whom I was shadowing, took the time to thoroughly explain how the medication works and how it would help her with her thyroid symptoms. The patient was relieved and was extremely appreciative. I thought to myself how rewarding it must have felt to be the pharmacist. From that experience, Dr. Robinson inspired me to be a pharmacist because I want to be there for my patients with the knowledge I gain in pharmacy school.

Example story of being "attentive to detail"

I interviewed a pharmacist who specialized in the field of oncology. She told me about a time when a doctor had ordered the wrong dosage for a chemotherapy medication and the pharmacist didn't catch it and had approved the medication to be given to the patient. The medication dosage was off by one decimal point and the patient took 10x more of the chemotherapy than was intended! The patient experienced drastic side effects but luckily survived. From this story, I realized the importance of why a pharmacist is the last line of defense in healthcare and learned that being attentive to detail is crucial to becoming a pharmacist. I recognize how important it is to be meticulous and I'm ready to take on that challenge.

Golden Questions — The Six Questions You Must Prepare For

In addition to *How to Answer Unexpected Questions* above, here are six questions that you will absolutely need to prepare for. Almost every interview will include the questions below so be prepared to answer them. Remember to put your answers into story format. This method really helps your interviewers see a good picture of you as a person.

1. Tell me about yourself.
2. Why pharmacy?
3. Behavioral/situational questions.
4. What are your strengths and weaknesses?
5. Tell me about your pharmacy experience.
6. Why this school?

Question 1 - Tell me about yourself.

This is often among the first few questions they ask during an interview. If this is the first question they ask you, start your introduction with a bit of background information such as your schooling and what you majored in. After that, instead of talking about where you were born, where you grew up, and your hobbies, focus on your journey of how you came to realize why you want to become a pharmacist. Your journey could be a moment in time when you realized that being a pharmacist is your calling. Your journey could also be a series of events coupled with plenty of research that led you to conclude that becoming a pharmacist is what you want to do for the rest of your life.

Another way to approach this question is to talk about your personality and values and how they fit as a pharmacist. Or use a mixture of the two. And at the tail end of your answer, summarize with three desirable characteristics you can bring to that pharmacy school and how those characteristics will contribute to your success as a future pharmacist.

Question 2 - Why pharmacy?

This question is similar to how you answer, "Tell me about yourself." Assuming that the interviewer asks both of these questions during the interview, try to tie in what you said in "Tell me about yourself" and expand on those characteristics. For example, if you talked about the journey that led you to want to become a pharmacist, then for this question talk about how being a pharmacist requires certain personality traits that you possess or highly value. If you talked about your personality and values and how they fit with being a pharmacist during the "Tell me about yourself" question, then talk about your complete journey and how it led you to pharmacy when you're answering "Why pharmacy?"

Everything you say at your interview should convey to the pharmacy school admissions that you love pharmacy and that you will be the happiest being in the entire planet if you become a pharmacist. You want your interviewer not just to think but to know that you are going to be the success story that every school wants to brag about.

Question 3 - Behavioral/Situational Questions.

During the interview, expect questions that are behavioral or situational based. A lot of these questions stem from the idea that **past actions indicate future performance.** This is a tough one. The key to answering situational types of question is to focus on your patients. Your customers, also known as your patients, are top priority, not the doctor. Most candidates make a big mistake by placing the doctor as first priority. Taking care of your patient should be top priority.

It's also important to focus on staying positive and looking at everyone's good side rather than focusing on their flaws. Being a pharmacist, a big part of your role is consoling patients who are in pain, in a bad mood, and will oftentimes vent their frustrations onto you. Therefore, having patience, empathy and compassion towards your patients is very important and should be heavily emphasized throughout the interview.

Example of situation-based questions:

1. You are working with a team and one team member is very negative and constantly complaining. What would you do?
2. You are at the pharmacy and a customer is very angry and rude and is yelling at your staff. What do you do?
3. You are at the pharmacy. There is a baby crying waiting for her meds, a doctor on the phone, and an elderly lady with a cane who looks like she's in pain. What do you do and who do you cater to first?
4. Tell us about a time when you had to deal with a difficult partner or coworker. How did you handle it? What would you have done differently?
5. Tell us about an accomplishment you are proud of and why.
6. Describe a difficult situation you were in and how you handled it.
7. Tell us about a time when you helped another individual with a problem and what the outcome was.

We recommend using the format below to answer these types of questions: Problem, Action, Result. It is a good format to use when you are trying to formulate answers in order to show off your leadership and management skills.

- **Problem** — What is the problem? Use this opportunity to develop the context of the problem and to show the interviewers how significant the problem was.
- **Action** — Say what you did and what your role was in this situation.
- **Result** — What was the result or outcome of your action or of your team's action?

Example answer to "Describe a difficult situation you were in and how you handled it."

I worked as a pharmacy technician for a year and I remember one day, when it was around peak time, there was a line out the door, phones were ringing off the hook, and a patient was very loud and angry and was making a scene. I happened to be working at the register when he showed up, and he was yelling at me. I understand that some patients who come to the pharmacy are in pain, they are upset possibly due to some other reason, and they are not directly upset at me. I try to see the good in people and, in this situation, instead of taking offense, I spoke to the customer calmly and nicely told him, "Sir, I understand you are very frustrated, but bear with us, we will get your prescription to you as soon as possible." With that the patient was able to calm down and the pharmacy staff members were able to do their job.

Question 4 - What are your strengths and weaknesses?

Strengths

Select strengths that align with the qualities of a good pharmacist. Follow up with a story describing how you demonstrated your strengths. Using the Problem, Action, Result method is another way to answer this type of question.

Weaknesses

There are many schools of thought on how to answer this question. Based on our experience, the best way to handle this question is naming a strength that could be a weakness. Every strength has a downside, oftentimes when there is too much of it. For example, you can be meticulous to the point where you disrupt workflow. You can be very passionate about pharmacy, so much so that your voice overshadows other people's opinions. You can be a team player but so much of a team player that you become disappointed when others are not on the same page. You can be too much of anything and that can be named a weakness.

"Being too meticulous" is a good example. This is a strength in the pharmacy world because it's better to be too meticulous than too careless. Being too careless can kill a patient, while being too meticulous could just be annoying to your peers. The secret to coming out strong with this question is focusing on your willingness to improve and how you will strengthen your weakness. Everyone is going to have a weakness, but it is their willingness to improve and their desire to overcome their weakness that makes them truly *stand out* as a candidate.

Why do interviewers ask you about your weaknesses? The reason they ask "What is your weakness?" is to see if you are a person with self-awareness, to understand how you think, and to find out if you are doing anything to improve your flaws. Whatever weakness you decide to share with your interviewers, always mention what steps you are taking to strengthen your flaws; that is exactly how you turn your weakness into a strength.

On another note, if it is an open interview, meaning your interviewers have access to your entire application, if you have any weaknesses in your application, this is a good time to bring them up. This is your time to turn any weaknesses in your portfolio into positives. Examples would include academic probation, having worked in a job that is unrelated to pharmacy for a few years or if you took a few years off to travel. Take what you learned during those difficult times and make it into a strength. For example, your previous job taught you great communication skills or your travels helped you learn about different cultures, which helps you relate to your patients better.

Question 5 - What pharmacy work experience do you have?

To interview well, it is highly recommended that you get pharmacy experience. *Any* pharmacy-related experience will do. Even a short-term stint helps! Shadowing a pharmacist for one day, working as a cashier in a pharmacy or volunteering at a student-run clinic for a few hours will help you tremendously with this question.

There are candidates who start out extremely personable in their interview but halfway into the interview we find that they have absolutely *no* pharmacy experience. Zero. Nada. The interviewer is going to have to address the elephant in the room. How do you know you want to be a pharmacist if you have absolutely *no* pharmacy experience?

Perhaps the applicant could say they imagined that being a pharmacist is the perfect path for them, but applicants who show that they want to be a pharmacist and have volunteered or worked with a pharmacist hold more credibility than one who has no pharmacy-related experience whatsoever. Despite how great the interview went, if the candidate did not have pharmacy experience, it casts a strong doubt on whether this path is truly the best for them. Admissions also want to accept students who are 100% sure they're going to make it through pharmacy school as graduating from pharmacy school is not an easy task.

If you do have pharmacy experience, fantastic! Focus on what you *learned* throughout your work or volunteer experience. Talk about the knowledge you gained in terms of what a pharmacist does. Even better, talk about a time when you saw your pharmacist help another patient and how that made you realize what a positive impact pharmacists have on our society and how you want to be just like them.

Question 6 - Why our school?

Do your research. Going to studentdoctor.net and browsing around the school's website is just a start. When you look at the website, pay attention to the curriculum offered. Each pharmacy school has something unique in their program that they offer to their students. Some schools have longer clinical training, some focus more on research, some focus more on patient care, some have classes taken together with medical students, some have interprofessional education ... and the list goes on. Ask yourself what makes their school unique. Find out what is unique about the school and let your interviewers know that you like those unique traits. Pick up the phone and call the school. See what kind of experience you will get. Connect with students from the school and take them out for lunch or a cup of coffee and *pick their brain*. Ask them what they like or dislike about the school. Ask what networking opportunities are available. Be creative. Take initiative and be proactive.

Interviewers want to know that you did your research and why you want to go to *their* particular school compared to another school. Much like dating, you should express all the reasons why their school is the one you want to go to, what makes their school so special, and why their school is the best match for you. The biggest turn-off for an interviewer is finding out that you are willing to go any school that accepts you. While this may be true for you, keep it to yourself.

During the Interview

How to speak during the interview

Interviews are intimidating and may feel like an interrogation, but it doesn't need to be this way. There's no "good cop, bad cop" routine, no detective hunkered behind a two-way mirror, and you definitely won't need to call your lawyer. Walk into your interview confidently (especially since you practiced so much) and maintain a calm and easygoing demeanor. Speak like you are having a heart-to-heart conversation with a close friend about your goals and dreams.

It's not just *what* you say, it's *how* you say it. Picture a person who is not confident. They are typically slouching, fidgety, mumbling, shallow breathing and not making eye contact. Now picture Wonder Woman or Superman. Despite them being popular comic book characters, they exhibit many traits of charisma and confidence. They stand tall, they inhale deep breaths, they walk with full strides, and they speak to others while making full eye contact. Imagine you are one of these superheroes and speak with confidence and charisma.

Practice answering your questions with a confident posture and voice. To perfect this, practice multiple mock interviews with friends, your significant other, coworkers or professional contacts. If you are embarrassed or shy and want unbiased opinion, practice with an interview coach (psst! we offer those services). Practicing your interview will prepare you to speak with confidence during the *real interview*.

What should I do when there is silence?

Silent pauses during the interview, especially after you finish answering a question, are perfectly normal. If you see your interviewer writing notes or if there are pauses between questions, don't be nervous or thrown off by it. Do not fill the silence with small talk, but instead wait patiently for the next question. Interviewer(s) may need time to gather their thoughts for the next question or may need to take notes in order to remember who they interviewed. Interviewers interview hundreds of candidates and taking notes during the interview helps them remember who you are. Be patient and smile.

How to read the interviewer

While you are answering your interview questions, pay close attention to your interviewer's body language. If you notice them nodding with approval or smiling like you hit a good point/something they agree with, you may have hit a sweet spot. Take note of what they liked, elaborate if needed and smile. If you notice that their eyes are glazing over, squinting or that they have a bored/questionable look, you need to steer the conversation back on track. You'll need to think on your feet and be able to quickly switch gears and transition into new topics. The key to doing all of this seamlessly? Practice.

Why do interviewers ask questions unrelated to pharmacy?

If the interviewer asks you multiple questions relating to your other jobs or experiences unrelated to pharmacy school such as, "What do you want to do? You tried this job, do you still want to do that?" or "Why did you pick pharmacy school over a master's program?" the interviewers are asking because they want to make sure you truly want to be a pharmacist and that pharmacy school is not just an alternative career or backup for medical school or a PhD program. Make sure the answer you give casts away any doubt about your interest and passion for pharmacy school. Emphasize that being a pharmacist is what you want for your career.

Don't answer: "I want to be a pharmacist because they make tons of money."

Do answer: "I know, without a doubt, that I want to help people and that pharmacy is my path to do so. I know it won't be easy, but I've done tons of research and am prepared. I am deeply committed to becoming a pharmacist."

The Last Question

After your interviewers have asked you all of their questions, they typically will end the interview with, "What questions do you have for us?" Prepare at least two to three questions to ask the interviewer. Ensure at least one of the questions is unique to the school you're interviewing for. The questions you ask must be well thought out and not questions that could be answered through the school's website. These questions should be answered by "insider" information or things that you can't find on their website. Why? Because it demonstrates that you cared enough about the school to do research, ask serious questions, and talk to people who have more than just a general knowledge of the surface-level topics covered by the school's informational material.

If you are entirely clueless about what to ask, here are some good but general questions:

1. I'm very interested in volunteering and helping the community, would you happen to know what volunteer opportunities <insert school name> offers their students?
2. What challenges do you see future pharmacists facing after they graduate?

After the Interview

If you can send a thank-you card to Mean Aunt Sally who gifted you those really ugly socks on your eighth birthday instead of the present you really wanted (we're not still bitter, we promise), you can definitely remember to thank your interviewer. Whether it's sending an email or a handwritten thank-you card to your interviewer(s), make sure you convey to them that you appreciate the time they took to speak with you. Make note of the proper spelling of their names during the interview so that you do not spell them incorrectly in your thank-you cards.

9

ADMISSIONS DECISIONS - THE GOOD, THE BAD, THE UGLY

"Success is a science; if you have the conditions, you get the result." – Oscar Wilde

Rejected

If Oprah can get fired from a job, you can get rejected from pharmacy school. This is a good opportunity to explore why you didn't get in. Did you give it your best shot? Did you dedicate yourself with conviction? If the answer is "No," you need to sit down and ask yourself why.

Assuming you gave it your best shot, rest assured knowing that you have the most important quality under your belt, complete dedication. Now we investigate!

- If you were denied admission from a school you're dying to get into, give that school a call and ask what you can improve on in your next application.
- If the admission committee felt you did not have sufficient work experience to succeed in their challenging program, your top priority should be getting a job or volunteering position to strengthen your case in the next application cycle.

- If the problem is your GPA, retake the classes you did not do so well in.
- If the problem is your personal statement, rewrite, edit, and polish with the help of your peers or even consider hiring a professional editor.
- If the problem is your PCAT score, you can restudy, hire a tutor and retake the test.
- If you feel that you could have done better during your interview, be sure to spend more time preparing and researching, and consider practicing with an experienced interview coach.
- It could also be the types of schools you applied to. You may have applied to schools that were a little out of reach with your grades and accomplishments in mind.

Consider applying to schools that are less competitive and/or in different geographical locations. Thomas Edison, the first inventor of the incandescent electric light bulb, once said, "I have not failed. I've just found 10,000 ways that won't work."[1] Embrace your inner Edison and remember there is no failure, only feedback.

Waitlisted a.k.a. The Waiting Game

There is still hope, just hang in there! As long as you have not received a rejection letter, you still have a chance of getting accepted. There are students who have received acceptance phone calls from schools up to the week before school begins. Get a leg up above the waitlist competition by notifying the pharmacy school by email/phone of any of the following waitlist boosters.

Waitlist Boosters:

- "Look, I'm being accomplished!" If you complete a significant project (like publishing a scientific/research paper or starting a non-profit organization related to pharmacy), make sure to update the pharmacy program admission committee of your recent accomplishments.
- "Look, I scored higher!" If you had a low PCAT score initially and retook the test after your interview, you should inform the school of your new/improved score as it is an important addition/enhancement to your application. If you got a lower score, shhh...
- "Look, I continue to be awesome!" If you want to be proactive, a unique approach is to write a follow-up letter of intent. Most students will wait and not push forward, but since you *really* want to be accepted to this particular school, include in your letter what you are currently doing now and how you are honing your skills to be a better future pharmacist. Describe how you will continue to pursue your dream.

Accepted

Congratulations! Your hard work has finally paid off. Now you can celebrate your achievement with your family and friends before the start of your pharmacy school adventure in the fall. You can go burn this book now. Please note that if you bought an eBook version, we don't recommend setting your phone/tablet on fire.

It is never too early to start preparing for pharmacy school. If you have not worked in a pharmacy before, go get your feet wet with some pharmacy basics such as memorizing the top 200 medications (brand, generic, and indications) and common pharmacy abbreviations. Getting these basics down before your school begins will not only give you a great head start, but it will also give you a nice little confidence boost as you embark on your pharmacy career.

10

HOW MUCH DOES A PHARMACIST MAKE?

"Dollar dollar bill, y'all." – Wu Tang Clan

ONE MAJOR FACTOR THAT is most likely motivating you to pursue becoming a pharmacist is money. Let's face it, financial freedom is what drives most of our behaviors. So, to get down to the meat of it, how much do pharmacists *actually* make?

Below are the numbers gathered in May 2017 by the Bureau of Labor Statistics that we have painstakingly compiled for you.[1] Note that salary varies by states due to the variance of costs of living and other factors.

National Employment and Mean Wage Estimates

Employment	Mean Hourly Wage	Mean Annual Wage
309,330	$58.52	$121,710

This table shows that there is a total of 309,330 pharmacists employed in the whole United States, and on average a pharmacist makes $58.52 an hour, which translates into $121,710 per year.

Percentile Wage Estimates

Percentile	10%	25%	50% (Median)	75%	90%
Hourly Wage	$42.03	$53.04	$59.70	$68.61	$76.64
Annual Wage	$87,420	$110,310	$124,170	$142,710	%159,410

This table shows that pharmacists in the 10th percentile earn $87,420 per year, which is less than the 6-figure incomes commonly believed to be what every pharmacist makes. The median annual wage is $124,170, which is slightly higher than the mean annual wage of $121,710.

Pharmacy Industries with Highest Levels of Employment

Industry	Employment	Percent of Industry Employment	Hourly Mean Wage	Annual Mean Wage
Health and Personal Care Stores	136,620	12.74	$58.37	$121,410
General Medical and Surgical Hospitals	74,060	1.35	$59.15	$123,040
General Merchandise Stores	24,180	0.75	$59.21	$123,160
Food and Beverage Stores	23,820	0.81	$58.33	$121,320
Merchant Wholesalers, Nondurable Goods	6,730	2.05	$57.70	$120,010

This table shows that most pharmacists (136,620) are working at the health and personal care stores, comprising 12.74% of the whole industry, as shown in the third column above. Although there are 74,060 pharmacists working in the general medical and surgical hospitals, it only represents 1.35% of the whole industry.

Top Paying Pharmacy Industries

Industry	Employment	Percent of Industry Employment	Hourly Mean Wage	Annual Mean Wage
Other Professional, Scientific, and Technical Services	70	0.01	$62.45	$129,890
Outpatient Care Centers	4,360	0.50	$62.44	$129,880
Offices of Physicians	4,880	0.19	$62.42	$129,840
Business, Professional, Labor, Political, and Similar Organizations	90	0.02	$61.94	$128,840
Pharmaceutical and Medicine Manufacturing	420	0.15	$61.88	$128,720

This table shows that pharmacists working in the top paying pharmacy industries get paid more than $60 per hour on average and the average annual income is close to 130k per year. The large numbers of pharmacists working at outpatient care centers and offices of physicians indicate that there are great job opportunities in these two industries.

Figure 1: Annual Mean Wage of Pharmacists by State

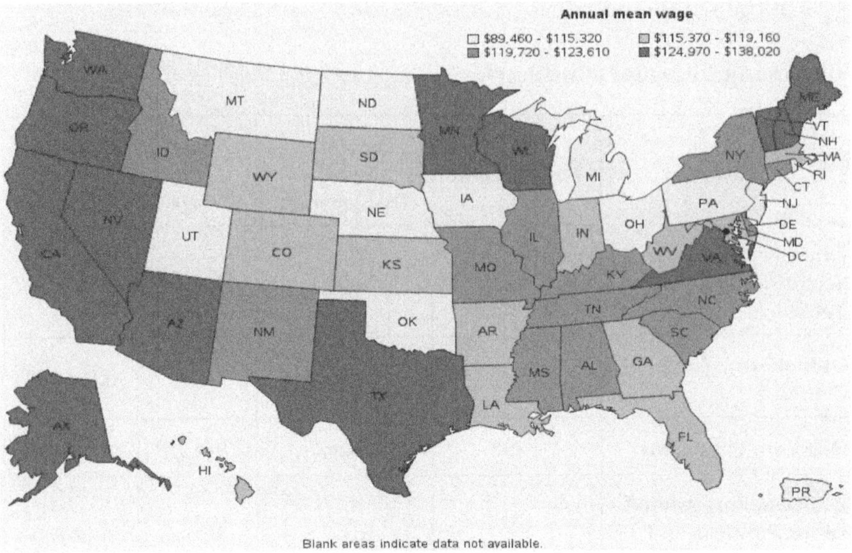

The darker shade represents a higher pharmacist wage. Pharmacists are making an annual mean wage of $124,970 - $138,020 in Washington, Oregon, California, Nevada, Arizona, Alaska, Texas, Minnesota, Wisconsin, Virginia, Maine, Vermont, and New Hampshire.

Table 1: Pharmacist's Average Hourly Wage Across the United States

US State	Average Annual Pharmacist Salary (May 2017)	Average Hourly Wage
Alabama	$122,020	$58.66
Alaska	$138,020	$66.36
American Samoa	$114,516	$55.06
Arizona	$124,970	$60.08
Arkansas	$117,670	$56.57
California	$136,730	$65.74
Colorado	$118,360	$56.90
Connecticut	$123,610	$59.43
Delaware	$122,230	$58.76
Florida	$118,780	$57.11
Georgia	$117,690	$56.58
Guam	$112,300	$53.99
Hawaii	$117,680	$56.58
Idaho	$119,790	$57.59
Illinois	$120,280	$57.83
Indiana	$115,640	$55.60
Iowa	$112,390	$54.03
Kansas	$117,370	$56.43
Kentucky	$121,970	$58.64
Louisiana	$115,560	$55.56

US State	Average Annual Pharmacist Salary (May 2017)	Average Hourly Wage
Maine	$125,680	$60.42
Maryland	$118,920	$57.17
Massachusetts	$116,820	$56.16
Michigan	$115,160	$55.37
Minnesota	$126,840	$60.98
Mississippi	$122,080	$58.69
Missouri	$123,610	$59.43
Montana	$113,080	$54.37
Nebraska	$113,720	$54.67
Nevada	$126,330	$60.74
New Hampshire	$127,900	$61.49
New Jersey	$115,110	$55.34
New Mexico	$122,670	$58.98
New York	$120,440	$57.90
North Carolina	$122,810	$59.04
North Dakota	$114,780	$55.18
Ohio	$114,950	$55.26
Oklahoma	$114,190	$54.90
Oregon	$125,850	$60.50
Pennsylvania	$113,830	$54.73
Puerto Rico	$89,460	$43.01
Rhode Island	$115,320	$55.44

US State	Average Annual Pharmacist Salary (May 2017)	Average Hourly Wage
South Carolina	$123,270	$59.26
South Dakota	$115,370	$55.47
Tennessee	$119,720	$57.56
Texas	$126,460	$60.80
Utah	$111,110	$53.42
Vermont	$134,090	$64.47
Virgin Islands	$102,430	$49.25
Virginia	$125,360	$60.27
Washington	$125,890	$60.52
Washington, D.C.	$123,490	$59.37
West Virginia	$118,150	$56.80
Wisconsin	$130,670	$62.82
Wyoming	$119,160	$57.29

This table shows that the average hourly wage ranges from $43.01 to $66.36 while the average annual wage ranges from $89,460 to $138,020.

States with the Highest Pharmacist Employment

State	Employment	Employment per Thousand Jobs	Location Quotient	Hourly Mean Wage	Annual Mean Wage
California	29,860	1.79	0.82	$65.73	$136,730
Texas	22,130	1.86	0.86	$60.80	$126,460
New York	21,890	2.38	1.10	$57.90	$120,440
Florida	20,510	2.44	1.12	$57.11	$118,780
Pennsylvania	13,630	2.36	1.09	$54.73	$113,830

This table shows California ranks first in terms of the number of pharmacists being employed, followed by Texas, New York, Florida, and Pennsylvania.

NOTES

Chapter 1: Don't Just Shine, Outshine

1. Rogers, Montana. "7 Incorrect Mark Twain Quotes." *New England Today*, 15 Nov. 2017, https://newengland.com/today/living/humor/mark-twain-didnt-say-that-incorrect-quotes/.

2. Foster, Jennifer. "Whether You Think You Can...Or Whether You Think You Can't...You're Right!" *Wall Street Insanity*, 25 Feb. 2013, https://wallstreetinsanity.com/whether-you-think-you-can-or-whether-you-think-you-cant-youre-right/.

3. Feloni, Richard. "Success Is Only 20% Skill, Says Tony Robbins — Here's What Makes up the Rest." *BI*, 5 Oct. 2017, https://www.businessinsider.com/tony-robbins-success-psychology-over-success-2017-10.

4. Dweck, Carol. *Mindset*. Random House Digital, Inc., 2008.

5. Covey, Stephen. *The 7 Habits of Highly Effective People*. Mango Media Inc., 2016.

Chapter 2: Is Pharmacy School Right for Me?

1. "Top Ten Reasons to Become a Pharmacist." *AACP*, https://www.aacp.org/resource/top-ten-reasons-become-pharmacist. Accessed 30 Sept. 2018.

2. "Graduating Student Survey, 2018 National Summary Report," *AACP*, July 2018, https://www.aacp.org/sites/default/files/2018-08/2018%20GSS%20National%20Summary%20Report.pdf. Accessed 30 Sept. 2018.

3. Hess, Abigail. "Here's How Much the Average Student Loan Borrower Owes when They Graduate." *CNBC*, 20 June 2018, www.cnbc.com/2018/02/15/heres-how-much-the-average-student-loan-borrower-owes-when-they-graduate.html.

4. PDI. https://pharmacymanpower.com/region.php. Accessed 12 Apr. 2018.

Chapter 3: What Can I Do with a PharmD?

1. *The ABC's of Community Pharmacy*. https://www.pharmacytimes.com/contributor/karen-berger/2018/02/the-abcs-of-community-pharmacy. Accessed 30 Sept. 2018.

2. Tsuyuki, Ross T. et al. "Pharmacists as Accessible Primary Health Care Providers: Review of the Evidence." *Canadian Pharmacists Journal : CPJ* 151.1 (2018): 4–5. *PMC*. Web. 30 Sept. 2018.

3. *Is Amazon a Threat to Independent Pharmacies?* https://www.pharmacytimes.com/contributor/lester-nathan-ms/2018/06/is-amazon-a-threat-to-independent-pharmacies. Accessed 30 Sept. 2018.

4. *ACCP - About Clinical Pharmacists*. https://www.accp.com/about/clinicalpharmacists.aspx. Accessed 30 Sept. 2018.

5. *Ambulatory Care Pharmacy Resident Q&A*. https://www.pharmacytimes.com/contributor/ekta-patel/2015/12/ambulatory-care-pharmacy-resident-qa. Accessed 30 Sept. 2018.

6. "Geriatric Pharmacist." *ExploreHealthCareers.Org*, 30 Sept. 2018, https://explorehealthcareers.org/career/geriatrics/geriatric-pharmacist/.

7. *Benefits & Rewards*. http://www.secnav.navy.mil/donhr/Benefits/Pages/Default.aspx. Accessed 30 Sept. 2018.

8. Tammie Lee Demler, BS. "Pharmacist Involvement in Hospice and Palliative Care." *U.S. Pharmacist*, 17 Mar. 2016, https://www.uspharmacist.com/article/pharmacist-involvement-in-hospice-and-palliative-care.

9. *What Is Managed Care Pharmacy? : Academy of Managed Care Pharmacy*. http://www.amcp.org/InformationForTertiary.aspx?id=9045. Accessed 30 Sept. 2018.

10. *Not Just Dispensing: The Unique Role of Pharmacists in an Outpatient Research Pharmacy*. https://www.pharmacytimes.com/publications/career/2016/pharmacycareers_may2016/the-unique-role-of-pharmacists-in-an-outpatient-research-pharmacy. Accessed 30 Sept. 2018.

11. *Academic Pharmacy as a Career Option - ASHP Connect*. 8 Jan. 2016, http://connect.ashp.org/blogs/thomas-szymanski/2016/08/01/academic-pharmacy-whats-that.

12. Mehvar, Reza. "Why Every Aspect of an Academic Pharmacy Career Should Be Viewed Through the Lens of Scholarship." *American Journal of Pharmaceutical Education* 81.1 (2017): 2. *PMC*. Web. 1 Oct. 2018.

13. *Nuclear Pharmacy: Scientific, Specialized, and Radioactive*. https://www.pharmacytimes.com/contributor/the-nontraditional-pharmacist/2018/02/nuclear-pharmacy-scientific-specialized-and-radioactive. Accessed 10 Jan. 2018.

14. Brohan, Mark. "Amazon Drops Hints on Why It Bought PillPack." *Digital Commerce 360*, 30 July 2018, https://www.digitalcommerce360.com/2018/07/30/amazon-drops-hints-on-why-it-bought-pillpack/.

Chapter 4: How Do I Choose Which Pharmacy School to Apply To?

1. https://pharmacyforme.org/wp-content/uploads/2018/03/psar-18-19-Table-4.pdf. Accessed 10 Oct. 2018.
2. Score Results | National Association of Boards of Pharmacy | NABP. (n.d.). Retrieved from https://nabp.pharmacy/programs/naplex/score-results/
3. Members., INSTRUCTIONS Click. "School Locator." AACP, https://www.aacp.org/resources/school-locator. Accessed 10 Oct. 2018.
4. *PDI*. https://pharmacymanpower.com/region.php. Accessed 12 Apr. 2018.
5. "Advanced Practice Pharmacist - California Pharmacists Association." *California Pharmacists Association*, https://cpha.com/app/. Accessed 12 Apr. 2018.

Chapter 5: How Much Does a PharmD Degree Cost?

1. Marquit, Miranda. "How Student Loan Interest Works | Student Loan Hero." *Student Loan Hero*, 7 Aug. 2018, https://studentloanhero.com/featured/how-student-loan-interest-works/.
2. "Graduate School Loans." Edvisors, https://www.edvisors.com/college-loans/federal/stafford/graduate/. Accessed 10 Oct. 2018.
3. Martin, Emmie. "90% of Americans Don't like to Cook—and It's Costing Them Thousands Each Year." CNBC, 27 Sept. 2017, https://www.cnbc.com/2017/09/27/how-much-americans-waste-on-dining-out.html. Accessed 13 Apr. 2018.

Chapter 6: Accelerated Pharmacy Programs

1. "Admissions | Albany College of Pharmacy and Health Sciences." *Albany College of Pharmacy and Health Sciences*, https://www.acphs.edu/admissions. Accessed 10 Feb. 2018.

2. *Pharmacy (PharmD) | MCPHS University*. https://www.mcphs.edu/academics/school-of-pharmacy/pharmacy/pharmacy-pharmd. Accessed 10 Feb. 2018.

3. "Pharmacy." *Ohio Northern University*, 7 Aug. 2015, http://www.onu.edu/pharmacy/pharmacy_degree_information.

4. *The University of Findlay - Doctor of Pharmacy Course Sequencing*. http://catalog.findlay.edu/en/current/Undergraduate-Catalog/Major-Requirements/College-of-Pharmacy/Doctor-of-Pharmacy-Course-Sequencing. Accessed 10 Feb. 2018.

5. School of Pharmacy, Ernest. "Ernest Mario School of Pharmacy." *Rutgers University*, https://newbrunswick.rutgers.edu/academics/ernest-mario-school-pharmacy. Accessed 10 Feb. 2018.

6. "Doctor of Pharmacy (Pharm.D.)." *South Dakota State University*, 7 Nov. 2018, https://www.sdstate.edu/pharmacy-and-allied-health-professions/doctor-pharmacy-pharmd.

7. "Doctor of Pharmacy Specific Policies, Procedures, and Documentation." *Home*, https://www.stjohns.edu/academics/schools-and-colleges/college-pharmacy-and-health-sciences/student-resources/doctorate/doctor-pharmacy-specific-policies-procedures-and. Accessed 10 Feb. 2018.

8. *Why STLCOP*. http://www.stlcop.edu/admissions/showcase/whystlcop.html. Accessed 10 Mar. 2018.

9. "Doctor of Pharmacy Program | College of Pharmacy." *The University of Rhode Island*, 1 May 2018, https://web.uri.edu/pharmacy/academics/pharmd/.

10. "Pre-Pharmacy Advantage Program." *University of the PACIFIC*, http://www.pacific.edu/academics/schools-and-colleges/thomas-j-long-school-of-pharmacy-and-health-sciences/academics/pre-pharmacy-advantage-program.html. Accessed 10 Mar. 2018.

11. "Pharmacy, PharmD, Direct Entry Admission | University of the Sciences." *University of the Sciences*, https://www.usciences.edu/philadelphia-college-of-pharmacy/pharmacy-pharmd/direct-entry-admission.html. Accessed 10 Mar. 2018.

Chapter 7: The Smart Application Game Plan

1. *Early Decision Deadline for Applicants – PharmCAS*. 4 Sept. 2018, http://www.pharmcas.org/event/early-decision-deadline-for-applicants/.

2. *Application Payment – PharmCAS*. http://www.pharmcas.org/preparing-to-apply/what-youll-need-to-apply/application-payment/. Accessed 10 Mar. 2018.

Chapter 8: Become Unrejectable and Get Accepted Anywhere

1. "Pharmacy College Admission Test | AACP." *AACP*, https://www.aacp.org/resource/pharmacy-college-admission-test. Accessed 10 Mar. 2018.

2. "What Is the PCAT?" *Kaplan Test Prep*, 3 Oct. 2001, https://www.kaptest.com/pcat/what-is-the-pcat.

3. *School Directory – PharmCAS*. http://www.pharmcas.org/school-directory/. Accessed 10 Feb. 2018.

Chapter 9: Admissions Decisions - The Good, The Bad, The Ugly

1. Daum, Kevin. "37 Quotes From Thomas Edison That Will Inspire Success." *Inc.*, 11 Feb. 2016, https://www.inc.com/kevin-daum/37-quotes-from-thomas-edison-that-will-bring-out-your-best.html.

Chapter 10: How Much Does a Pharmacist Make?

1. *Pharmacists*. 30 March 2018, https://www.bls.gov/oes/current/oes291051.htm.

ACKNOWLEDGEMENTS

A BIG, FAT THANKS to Emily Huang for whipping this book into shape. Also, many thanks to Kiely Omura who helped with editing the book as well. Thank you both for making us appear to be decent writers. Ken Darrow did an amazing job with the final proofreading of the book. We can't thank you enough. Thanks to Christina and Dhruv who contributed their essays and insights into this book.

To the many friends, colleagues, and brothers from Kappa Psi Pharmaceutical Fraternity whose input helped to shape the content of our book. We must also thank Dr. Justin Williams for sharing valuable tips and actionable plans that worked wonders for many of his students who wanted to become pharmacists. Justin's caring nature and enthusiasm to help others achieve their dreams has taught us so much about human compassion, an exemplary quality that is highly sought after in the healthcare profession. We are deeply grateful for our alma mater, Western University of Health Sciences, that shaped us (with tough loves) into who we are today.

Jenna Giacomin and Celina Chang also kindly reached out to us to share their experience on how they got into an accelerated pharmacy program. Thank yowithu for the gesture; your incredible insights helped to expand the scope of our content.

And thank you so much to Devon Williams, John Somerville, Frederick Lo, Chris Ishisoko, Ryan Khaleghi, Judy Liao, and Cindy Lin for their input and edits in this book. A special thanks to Joshua Yin for all his emotional support and delicious home cooked food.

ABOUT THE AUTHORS

Ryan Ngov, PharmD graduated from Western University of Health Sciences and founded Reshape The Mind, Inc., a consulting company that provides mentoring services, academic counseling, and career guidance for high school and college students. He is an expert at taking even high achievers to greater levels of success, which is evidenced by their acceptances to Stanford, Brown, UCLA and other highly competitive colleges, graduate, and professional schools in the United States.

Kathy Chow, PharmD graduated from Western University of Health Sciences and started PharmacyInterview.com, an interview coaching and consulting company for those aspiring to be pharmacists. A seasoned expert at shaping pharmacy candidate applications and interview coaching, Kathy endeavors to showcase the candidates' best version of themselves. She works with students from all over the world to maximize their application portfolios and help them excel in interview after interview.

Q&A

Why did you write this book?
We wrote this book to help people who are interested in pursuing a career in pharmacy a.k.a. you! We want to help you get a good grasp of what to expect if you become a pharmacist, whether or not being a pharmacist is a good path for you, and **how to succeed in your quest to get into pharmacy school** to become a pharmacist.

How did you get all the costs of attending pharmacy schools? How reliable are those numbers?
Some schools provided all the estimated costs on their websites and for those we just copied and pasted them into our tables. Many schools only show one year of tuition and fees; we estimated the following year costs by assuming a 5% inflation rate. A few schools reported the cost per unit and for those we have to manually calculate the tuition, taking into account the total number of units the students need to complete to graduate and again factoring in the inflation rate of 5% every year. As inflation rate usually ranges from 3% to 5%, the numbers we presented is of the higher end estimates, meaning they might be slightly higher than the actual costs of tuition and fees.

Why are there so many darn tables in the book?
These tables are not available anywhere on the internet and they are extremely valuable resources for when you are trying to decide which schools to apply to. Originally, during the dark ages when we were applying to pharm school, we had to compile the data and organize it on our own on top of our schooling. Use them, love them, and thank us with a 5 star rating on Amazon.

Do you offer private coaching for students who need more help with their pharmacy school application?

Yes! On top of what's in this book, we have a menu of services which provide more hands-on, customized guidance for students looking to get into pharmacy school. These services are by appointment only. If you want to reach Ryan, you can find him at www.reshapethemind.com. If you want to reach Kathy, you can find her at www.pharmacyinterview.com.

PLEASE, PAY IT FORWARD!

Thank you.

We know that you could have picked any book to read, but you chose this book and we are extremely grateful. A lot of work went into this book since we wanted to give others the help we wish we had. If this book helped you (or didn't - we're open to constructive criticism), please take a minute to leave feedback at:

feedback@reshapethemind.com

If you have friends/coworkers who would benefit from this book, share it and spread the word!

Want to help us out with our mission?
Leave a review on Amazon!

We love reading them and will edit our next book with your feedback in mind.

No, seriously, we'll read your review so please give feedback.

In all seriousness, we wish you the best of luck, an endless supply of caffeine, and a cute puppy to warm your cold, dead heart after you're done with pharm school applications.

Sincerely,

Kathy and Ryan